PAPERMAKING IN LINCOLNSHIRE

1600-1900

by

Hugh Nott

The Society for Lincolnshire History and Archaeology
2008

First published by the Society for Lincolnshire History and Archaeology 2008

© Hugh Nott and
the Society for Lincolnshire History and Archaeology

ISBN 978 0 903582 33 9

British Library Cataloguing in Publication Data
A CIP catalogue record for this book is available from the British Library

Front cover illustrations: a painting of Leasingham Mill in the 1930s by Karl Wood (*courtesy of Lincolnshire County Council, reproduced by permission of the Benedictines of Pluscarden Abbey*)(see Fig. 36); illustration of a sixteenth century paper mill from *Theatrum Machinarum Norum* published by G A Bockler in 1662 (see Fig. 1); page of accounts dated 1802 on paper bearing watermark of Christopher Dinsdale (*courtesy of Lincolnshire Archives Office and Mark Deyncourt*)(see Fig. 30).

Designed by Susan Unsworth at the Heritage Trust of Lincolnshire
Printed in the UK by G W Belton Ltd, Gainsborough

Contents

Acknowledgements

I am greatly indebted for the vast help received from many sources. It has been a pleasure to gather together all of the information concerning the Lincolnshire paper industry. In particular I would like to record my thanks to the following descendants of Thomas Clarke (1725-1804), one of the first papermakers in Tealby: Helen Owen (nee Clarke), fourth great-granddaughter; Deborah Clarke, sixth great-granddaughter and Steve Kibble, fourth great grandson. Their enthusiasm has been invaluable. I would also like to thank all of the staff at the Lincolnshire Archives; if it had not been for their record keeping, this book would have been impossible. In particular, I would like to thank Peter Noon and his colleagues for producing the photographic images of the Tealby watermarks and Mark Deyncourt for permission to use the images from the Tennyson d'Eyncourt Collection in the Lincolnshire Archives in this book. Grateful thanks are also due to Sir Lyonel Tollemache for permission to use his archives and incorporate details relating to the Houghton Mill from 1825 to 1896.

Thanks are also due to the Mormon Church for their online genealogy records; the Lincolnshire County Council Library Service at Lincoln, Louth and Market Rasen; The Collection, Art and Archaeology in Lincolnshire, for the copy of the painting of Leasingham paper mill by Karl Woods (1930), reproduced by permission of the Benedictines of Pluscarden Abbey; the Welholme Gallery for a copy of the Bryant (1828) Map; the Public Library at Grimsby; Wookey Hole Paper Mill at Wells, Somerset; Rachel Grasham (fourth great-granddaughter of Michael Gresham) for the photographs of Lower Papermill; Colin Grasham (fourth great-grandson of Michael Gresham); John Howard for photographs of Tealby Vale and to Peter Rhodes for permission to use them; Jon Sass for his foreword and the copy of the copper engraving of Barrow on Humber; Ken Redmore for redrawing the location maps; Beryl Kelly (fourth grandniece of Edward Stourton) for some family history; John and Ella Sivil of Tealby Thorpe Watermill for advice on watermills; Stewart Squires for permission to incorporate his 1992 survey findings on the Lower Papermill at Tealby; Eileen Robson, Karen Warner, Ruth Tinley, David Robinson OBE, Christine Harrison and Simon Pawley for useful comments and Graham Wallace and Leslie Evans for help with editing. Special thanks are due to David Start, Stewart Squires and the Society for Lincolnshire History and Archaeology for all the work needed to convert the original draft into this final publication.

This book is dedicated to my darling wife, Penny

Hugh Nott
July 2008

A note on pre-decimal British currency

Monetary values in this book are derived from historical documents and are shown in British pre-decimal values of pounds, shillings and pence (£ s d). There were twelve (old) pennies in a shilling and twenty shillings in a pound. Conversions are generally unhelpful because of inflation, but may be carried out on the basis that five (new) pence is the equivalent of one shilling (= twelve old pennies).

For instance: £4 4s 6d (or £4/4/6) = £4.22½
10s 6d (or 10/6) = 52½p
5s. (or 5/-) = 25p

Foreword

I am delighted at last we have a study relating to watermills in Lincolnshire. Their role in providing motive power for many traditional industries besides grain processing has been greatly overshadowed by the more visual and romanticised windmill. Today we take for granted the availability of inexpensive paper for myriad uses. For those that remember the huge Dixon's paper mill on West Marsh Grimsby it will be difficult to imagine the typical small handmade paper mill. The earliest records of a paper mill in Lincolnshire are of that at Leasingham Moor near Sleaford by 1617. Scant information also survives of another at Caistor by 1668.

The process of reducing the raw materials of handmade paper to produce a thick solution or 'stuff' was similar to that used in fulling woven woollen cloth to felt and clean it. The former important woollen industry in Lincolnshire had declined considerably during the post medieval period but as water power and the availability of clean water were vital to both fulling and papermaking, it is hardly surprising that several fulling mills were converted to papermaking.

Hugh Nott is to be commended for the effort he has expended in teasing out the information relating to the individual mills from many obscure sources. My earlier researches regarding the story of the mills of Tealby taught me how fraught this can be and earlier written inaccuracies have been corrected by his diligent research. He has even discovered examples of Lincolnshire papermaker's watermarks, disproving earlier learned assumptions that good quality white paper was not being produced in this county.

Tragically, because all but one of these mills had ceased production by the 1840s and converted to corn milling (or other uses) no plant or specifications had survived. Hugh's detective work has, however, given us a good idea of the size and operation of individual mills.

The evidence that survives indicates the majority of the county's mills were small low-tech units which Hugh has estimated were able to produce approximately five tons of paper per mill per annum. It is not known what ratio of coarser wrapping paper to high quality white paper was produced. A number of factors, however, made these small mills less viable and brought about their demise before the middle of the nineteenth century. The small, often rural, mills of Lincolnshire, isolated from the growing transport infrastructure, appear to have been under-capitalised and struggled to remain competitive.

Much more information has been collated on the papermakers and their business acumen. Hugh has woven a fascinating social history of inter-marriage and business links between the mills. Through contact with the descendants of some of the master papermakers he has been able to put flesh on the bones of these skilled artisans.

When Houghton paper mill near Grantham ceased production in the 1880s it closed a chapter on an important industry in the county. This publication offers a valuable study of a bygone industry and its skilled practitioners. It will be welcomed by those interested in the industrial archaeology, local and family history within our large and diverse county and add valuable archive material of the paper making industry within England.

Jon Sass
Lincolnshire Mills Group

SEVEN BROTHERS WHOSE AGES AGGREGATE 513 YEARS

The seven Clarke brothers, all papermakers, pictured in 'The Sphere' 16 November 1907. This remarkable papermaking family were the great great grandsons of Thomas Clarke, papermaker, born in Tealby in 1725. (Front row) Adam; Thomas; Paul; Joseph; (back row) Andrew; John; Silas. (see also Fig. 33)

Introduction

The Chinese developed papermaking using rags and rice stalks in about AD100. The process came to Europe in the twelfth century; the first recorded use was in Spain in 1150. The first paper mill in England was recorded in about 1495. Called Sele Mill and owned by John Tate, a citizen of London, it was located on a tributary of the River Lea below Hertford. In 1588 a German entrepreneur, Herr Spielman, owned a paper mill in Dartford, Kent. He was jeweller to both Elizabeth I (1558-1603) and James I (1603-1625); he restored the jewellery which Elizabeth had inherited from her father, Henry VIII. He was given sole rights in England to make white writing paper and control over other types of papermaking. In 1589 Elizabeth gave him a licence for ten years to be the sole buyer of linen rags, old fishing nets and leather shreds for making all sorts of white paper. Nobody else was allowed to build a paper mill without his consent. This licence was renewed in 1597 for a further fourteen years. Thus he had a total monopoly; this may have been a form of censorship by controlling the means of writing and printing. Herr Spielman was knighted Sir John Spilman by James I at Dartford. Spilman died in 1626. By 1700 there were about 100 paper mills in England, and by 1800 the number had grown to over 400.

Lincolnshire is a large sparsely populated county in the East Midlands of England. It is a major farming and food-production area of about 600,000 hectares. The population has grown from 208,000 in 1801, to 500,000 in 1901, to about 650,000 in the present day.

The earliest record of a papermaker in Lincolnshire is at Evedon near Sleaford. In 1617 Daniel Turner was described as a paperman when his daughter was baptised; he probably worked at the paper mill at Leasingham Moor, which continued to produce paper until 1829. The next recorded mill was at Tealby, near Market Rasen; it was in production from about 1700 until 1829. The third mill, in operation from 1731 to 1890, was situated at Houghton (now a suburb of Grantham). The fourth mill was at West Deeping, from 1733 to 1745. A second mill in Tealby began in 1763 and finished in 1834. The sixth mill in Lincolnshire was at Barrow on Humber; it only functioned from about 1780 until about 1800. A mill at Louth was in production from about 1794 until 1843. A third mill in Tealby, the eighth in Lincolnshire, began in 1800 and finished in 1829.

In order to give a clearer documentation of the different aspects, the section on Tealby papermakers includes some repetition of sections elsewhere in the book that relate to paper mills.

Papermaking

Prior to the mid nineteenth century the chief raw material for making writing or better quality paper was white cotton or linen rags; these were mainly imported from Europe where there was a plentiful supply. The rags were sorted, cut into small pieces (2″ x 4″) and had the buttons, hooks and lengths of whalebone removed before being boiled with caustic soda. In the early days of papermaking the rags were beaten using water-powered hammers for between twelve and thirty-six hours to produce a smooth pulp called 'stuff' (with a concentration of about 3-5% solids). Later, in the middle of the eighteenth century, the rag-engine or 'hollander' was invented in Holland. It consisted of an oval-shaped vessel with a partition partly along its length to make a continuous trough. On one side of the trough was a roller with teeth which hammered and beat the rags to a pulp. The beating process removed traces of dirt and caustic soda and separated the fibres, causing them to increase their water holding capacity. The stuff then passed to a 'stuff chest' where it was kept agitated before being passed to the 'vat'. The vat was then filled with the stuff and agitated by means of a pole or 'potching stick'. Later the agitation was mechanised using a paddle called a 'hog'. Shallow rectangular wooden trays, with bottoms made of reed or straw or phosphor bronze wire, were then dipped in the vats of stuff by the 'vatman'. The trays had a removable frame called a 'deckle' on top, which stopped the fibres from washing over the edge. The trays were then shaken using a particular motion to make the fibres intertwine and form a sheet. The vatman then passed the tray to his co-worker the 'coucher' (from the French word *coucher*, to lie down). The coucher removed the sheets of fibre and laid them on a woollen felt. Another felt was then laid on top and a pile of 144 sheets of paper (six quires) and felts known as a 'post' was formed. The post was then placed in a press to remove the excess water. The press was usually very cumbersome and required the strength of all the workers to turn the screw. A third worker, a 'layer' or 'layman' then removed each sheet of paper and placed them in a pile without the felts. The pile was then pressed again. 'Spurs' of four or five sheets of paper were then hung to dry in the drying room or drying loft on ropes woven from cow or horsehair that had been coated with beeswax. The drying process took up to a week. While making the initial sheet, some of the 'stuff' inevitably flowed under the deckle, which caused slightly

Fig. 1: A sixteenth century paper mill. Notice the waterwheel, the hammers being lifted by the camshaft, the vat containing the 'stuff', the 'vatman' shaking and draining the wire-bottomed tray, the 'coucher' pressing the sheets of paper' the pressed sheets drying on overhead lines and the finished bundles of paper. (from: Theatrum Machinarum Norum published by G A Bockler, 1662)

ragged edges on the paper sheets known as deckles. During drying, the paper contracts and becomes wrinkled and cockled. If the paper was to be used for writing, the sheets were 'sized' by dipping them in a tub of hot gelatine made from animal skins, bones and hooves. Later, other sizing products were used e.g. rosin (a resin resulting from distilling crude turpentine) or gelatine with casein (milk protein), starch and minerals such as alum. This made the unsized (waterleaf) sheet resistant to ink. The sheets were then dried and put through a roller to give a smooth wrinkle-free surface. From the early nineteenth century, rosin was added to the 'stuff' to size the paper. This eliminated one operation in the process.

The watermark was produced when tinned copper wire was sewn in intricate patterns on the mesh bottom of the trays. One of the early watermarks was a jester's head in a cap with bells, hence 'foolscap'. Watermarks were only used on good quality white paper and from 1794 most watermarks also had year date marks. This was to permit refunds of excise tax on exported paper. The excise tax was finally abolished in 1861. Papermakers only used fine linen and cotton rags for making high quality writing and printing paper and they used materials such as old hemp ropes, netting, poor quality rags, canvas and old sacks to make common brown, whited brown and blue papers for wrapping and packaging. Sailors could earn a little extra money by selling old ropes to dealers, who sold them to the paper and bookbinding trades; hence the expression 'money for old rope'.

A Frenchman, Nicholas Louis Robert, invented the first papermaking machine in 1798. Bryan Donkin further developed the machine in England for Henry Fourdrinier who had a paper mill at Dartford in Kent. The first machine was installed at Frogmore Mill in Hertfordshire. It was known as the Fourdrinier machine and began to be used from about 1804. The machine consisted of a continuously moving, endless wire conveyor belt. All the processes were automated and the speed of the belt determined the grade and weight of paper being produced. The increasing adoption of the Fourdrinier machine resulted in the gradual demise of the hand papermaking process. A cylinder machine was introduced in 1809.

According to Shorter[1] the peak year for producing handmade paper was 1805. In that year 16,500 tons of paper were made and only 557 tons (3%) were made by machine. By 1824 there were 12,750 tons of handmade paper and 14,459 tons (53%) of machine-made paper. In 1840 handmade paper had declined to 9,935 tons and machine-made paper reached 33,463 tons (77%).

Most paper mills only had one vat, and a team of three men (vatman, coucher and layer) could produce from five to eight reams (about 500 sheets a ream) of handmade paper a day. This was equivalent to about five tonnes of paper a year which would require about 25 tonnes of rags (about five pounds of rag was required for each pound of paper). In addition to the three principal workers there would be someone in charge of the rag-beating and several women who sorted the rags and graded, sorted, counted, glazed and packed the paper. In total there would be ten to fifteen people involved. In 1805 the men would earn between twelve and thirty shillings a week, depending on their output. In 1829 Timothy Piper estimated that the total wages would be about £10 a week for a singled-vatted paper mill. The productivity of the new machines was far greater and by 1840 very few paper mills were still making paper by hand. When Timothy Piper, the manager of Samuel Evans's five-vatted mill at Darley, near Derby, was negotiating to lease a paper mill in Tealby in 1829, he wrote *'the depression of the paper trade is so great in consequence of ... machines for making paper ... except I can make the best white* [paper] *... which cannot be made by machines'*. The environment was hot and humid and the working conditions were arduous, particularly for the vatman; he was constantly stooping with his hands in and out of water. He required great patience and skill to produce consistent thickness and surfaces of the paper. The apprenticeships for papermakers lasted for seven years.

Fig. 2: An early woodcut of papermaking
(from: The Art of Handmade Paper by V Studley, 1990)

Paper Mills

The main requirements for successful papermaking were: a reliable source of clean water without iron deposits (which caused staining); a location suitable to have a mill wheel; adequate supplies of rags and other raw materials; a skilled workforce and adequate transport to bring the raw materials to the mill and to deliver the finished paper to the customers. In the early days of papermaking the power derived from the waterwheel was needed to pulp the rags. The size of the waterwheel was important because it acted as a continuous series of buckets on the end of a series of levers. The weight of water in each bucket, the number of buckets and the diameter of the wheel largely determined the power of the mill. Many waterwheels were about eighteen feet in diameter with buckets spaced at twelve to eighteen inch centres. The most efficient wheels were about 65% to 70% efficient and were called over-shot; i.e. the water filled the buckets at the top of the wheel. This required an eighteen foot head of water for an eighteen foot wheel. Another common type of wheel was the breast-shot wheel (about 55% to 60% efficient). In this case the water filled the buckets at about 'nine o'clock'. If they were filled at between nine and ten o'clock they were called high breast wheels and if they were filled below nine o'clock, they were called low breast wheels. As a rough guide twelve cubic feet of water a second should give one horse power for every foot of fall. Another type of waterwheel was the under-shot wheel where the wheel is turned by the flow of the stream, rather like the paddle on a Mississippi steamboat (except in that case the engine of the boat turns the paddles causing the boat to moved in relation to the water). These wheels are only about 25-35% efficient but they do not need any head of water. The power derived from the waterwheel was converted by gears to drive a wooden stamper to break up the rags required for the paper.

An interesting and informative advertisement appeared in the *Lincoln, Rutland and Stamford Mercury* in 1806:

'To be sold. A single vat mill, with extensive drying lofts and every other building and convenience for an extensive trade abundantly supplied with water from a fine rivulet, that stuff may be got for two vats, also fine spring water, to supply engine, of a peculiar quality that excellence so desirable in the colour of paper; also so centrally situated in the County of Lincoln as to be at a moderate distance from almost every principal market town therein, where rags in any quantity are readily procured - the machinery very powerful, with about four acres of rich meadow land adjoining.'

Potential purchasers were requested to apply to Mr Newcomb at Stamford. There is no identification of the precise location of the mill, however, it is worth noting the references to water quality, the power of the stream, the importance of location and the source of the raw material. Note also that the mill was using domestic rather than imported rags. The engine was the machine used to beat the rags to pulp.

Tealby Paper Mills

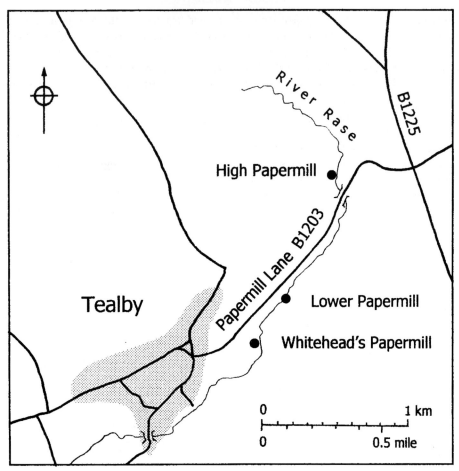

Fig. 3: The location of the Tealby paper mills

Tealby is situated on the edge of the Lincolnshire Wolds about three miles east-north-east of Market Rasen and the River Rase has its source in the hills above Tealby. Tealby was previously known as *Tavelesbi, Tauelesbi, Tauelebi* and *Teuelesby* and many other variations. At one time it was thought that 'Tealby' was derived from the Anglo-Saxon word *taefl*, meaning chessboard or table, and from the Old Danish word *by*, meaning a farmstead or village. Hence, table village, possibly indicating a flat-topped hill. However, more recent studies by Professor Kenneth Cameron suggest that the name Tealby is probably derived from the East Germanic tribal-name *Taifali* and the Old Danish word *by*. Detachments of the *Taifali* are recorded in Britain in the early fifth century. Therefore, Tealby probably means the village of the *Taifali* people. The Viking army settled in Lincolnshire in the late ninth

century. Some Old Danish names still survive in Tealby, such as *thorp* a secondary settlement, 'beck' from *bekkr* meaning a stream and *smooting* a narrow passage between houses.

When the Domesday Book was compiled in 1086 there were fifteen mills and three mill sites in Tealby. In this context, mills meant a pair of stones used for grinding corn rather than individual buildings. Some buildings may have had more than one pair of stones. Most mills would have been water-powered but oxen or mules may have driven others and some could have been just hand-operated mills. At that time all mills were taxed, hence their inclusion in the Domesday Book. The River Rase had a major influence on the village for the next 800 years, firstly for grinding corn, tanning leather and for fulling

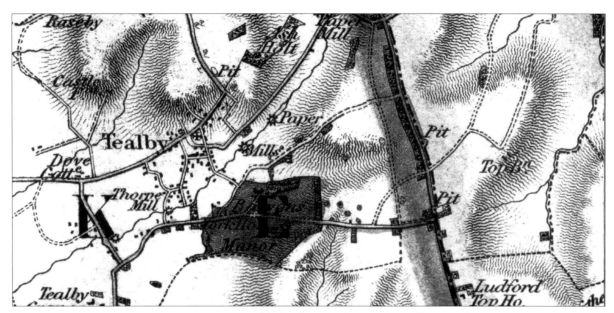

Fig. 4: Bryant's map of 1828 showing three paper mills at Tealby

woollen materials and then from the early eighteenth century until about 1840, for papermaking. A fulling mill was used to pound woven woollen cloth in water to shrink it and increase the density of the material by causing the fibres to bind together, thus making it stronger, smoother and softer. The woollen cloth was mixed with Fuller's Earth and urine to clean it and to remove the oil that was added during weaving. The components of fulling mills and paper mills were fairly similar and it was quite common to convert fulling mills into paper mills. Mills were sometimes used for grinding corn during the winter months and for fulling cloth during the summer months. Two former corn mills are still situated in the village. One (Watermill House, Sandy Lane) is now a residence and Thorpe Mill which still retains the original wheel and equipment and is still operated occasionally. There were three paper mills on the River Rase at Tealby. All three mills are shown on the Bryant's 1828 map (Fig. 4).

High Papermill

The first paper mill in Tealby was Pad Mill, later known as the High or Top Papermill. This was referred to as mill number 207 in the Excise Lists of 1816 and was situated about 1900 yards north east of Tealby Church, at the bottom of Bully Hill (N.G.R. TF 170920). Matthew Stourton or his son Edward (the elder) probably converted this mill from a fulling mill sometime before 1700.

The insurance policy[10] taken out by Edward Stourton (the younger) in 1755 (Fig. 5) reads as follows:

'Edward Stouerton of Louth in the County of Lincoln Papermaker. On his Paper mill, Drying Rooms, Ware rooms and offices adjoining Only in the Parish of Tilby ... Stone Brick Timber tiles and Thatched in his own Occupation not exceeding One hundred and Sixty pounds ...'

In 1791 it was described as *'a messuage then used as several habitations with paper mill adjoining'*. The insurance policy taken out in 1794 by Michael Gresham describes it as High Papermill, stone and tiled. It was warranted to have no stove or steam engine. When John Clarke insured the mill in 1801, the policy describes it as *'paper mill, saull room drying lofts and store room brick built and tiled all adjoining in Tealby aforesaid having a stove therein £700. Warranted to have no steam engine in adjoining to or communicating with the above building'.* The saull or salle or sol room was the room used to sort and pack the paper.

In 1825 the mill was repaired at a cost of £204. This included £68 for new engines and press, £12 for a stuff chest and £6 for new cogs for the flywheel. In August 1827 it was estimated that repair work valued at £197 was required. This included a new water wheel and shade (£65), new mill head and penstock gate (£6), new pit wheel and flywheel gearing. A sale advertisement in

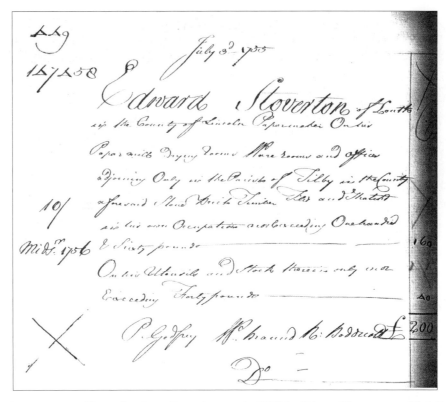

Fig. 5: The insurance certificate for the policy taken out in 1755 by Edward Stourton on High Papermill
(courtesy of the Corporation of London, Guildhall Library)

February 1829 described the mill as '*an old established single vatted Papermill and the requisite drying houses, ... The mill is adapted to the manufacture of paper of the best quality and possesses also a most desirable advantage in the first use of a very fine stream of spring water, with a spacious dam and good descents*. Between February and August of that year a lot of correspondence took place between Timothy Piper from Darley, near Derby, and George Tennyson or his agent William Cooper. Timothy Piper wanted to lease the mill; he had been the manager of Samuel Evans's five-vatted paper mill at Darley for many years and was worth '*£1,400 to £1,500*'. Darley paper mill was where Thomas Clarke, the nephew of John Clarke, the former tenant of this mill was working at that time. Samuel Evans gave the following reference '*Mr Timothy Piper has saved some money and is a prudent man, and I think may safely be taken as a tenant if they can agree on terms*'.

Timothy Piper wrote '*the depression of the paper trade is so great in consequence of ... machines for making paper ... except I can make the best white* [paper] *... which cannot be made by machines*'. He signed a memorandum

of agreement on 12 March 1829 to lease the mill for 21 years at £100 a year. George Tennyson would spend £340 to repair the buildings and Timothy Piper would spend £500 repairing the mill machinery. However, when he got home to Darley and obtained more estimates for the work, he estimated that he would require £1,880 to repair and run the mill for six months. The repairs included a new water wheel, a new pit wheel and flywheel, three pinions and two new engines plus about £300 for lead work on two engines, one chest and one vat. Thus it seems that the mill was in a poor state of repair and the work needed in 1827 was never carried out. Interestingly, he estimated the running costs for six months as follows:- wages for papermakers - £250; rags - 10 Hund[redweight]/wk at 30/-/ Hund - £390; skins for size - £60; coals - £30 and duty - £200. He wrote to William Cooper, George Tennyson's agent, that '*I am of the opinion that £2,000 will not more than cover the expense which is at least £700 more than I actual have. The paper trade is now so flat that except you can give 6, 9 or 12 months credit you can not do business. I hope you will not think it caprice on my part for given it up. I must endeavour to find something what*

Fig. 6: High (Top) Papermill Cottages in 1939.
Looking south towards Papermill Lane

my little capital can meet'. He crossed out his signature on the agreement, much to the annoyance of George Tennyson. In August 1829 Timothy Piper wrote to say that he would manage the mill for George Tennyson for £100 a year plus a house. It seems that the paper industry was in a poor situation and the mill was in a poor state of repair and no more paper was made at that mill. George Tennyson's rental record shows that there was no tenant of the mill in 1830.

The mill cottages (fig. 6) were destroyed by fire in about 1950 when the Bagley family lived there. The Tealby fire engine attended the fire; it was a trailer pulled by a vehicle belonging to Walter Leaning (a butcher in Tealby). This was the only time that the fire engine was ever used. Private John Bagley, who was killed in France in 1915 in World War I, had lived at these cottages. Interestingly, there was a Robert Bagley who witnessed the inventory of the papermaker, Robert Harness in 1721, and a John Bagley who was allotted 4¼ acres in the enclosure of 1792 to 1795. So the Bagley family had long connections with Tealby.

The owners and occupiers of High Papermill were:

Date	Owner	Occupier/Tenant
<1718	Edward Stourton (the elder)	Humphrey Lees
1720	Edward Stourton (the elder)	Robert Harness
1721	Edward Stourton (the elder)	Thomas Harness
1731	Edward Stourton (the elder)	William Hemsworth
1746	Edward Stourton (the elder)	Edward Stourton (the younger) ?
1753	Edward Stourton (the younger)	?
1756	John and Matthew Stourton	?
1763	John and Matthew Stourton	Thomas Houghton
1791	John and Matthew Stourton	Michael Gresham
1793	Edward and Joseph Stourton	Michael Gresham
1799	Edward and Joseph Stourton	John Clarke
1800	George Tennyson	John Clarke
1804	George Tennyson	John Clarke
1816	George Tennyson	Thomas Brice
1825	George Tennyson	Representatives of Thos. Brice (Benjamin Clark as papermaker)
1826	George Tennyson	John Haddack and Isaac Robinson
1830	George Tennyson	vacant?

Lower Papermill

The second mill to be used for papermaking in Tealby was Springside Mill, later known as Lower Papermill, which was mill number 206 in the Excise Lists of 1816. It was situated about 700 yards north east of Tealby Church (N.G.R. TF 162910). In early editions of the Ordnance Survey maps there is a spring identified near the building, which was presumably the reason for calling it Springside Mill. An insurance policy taken out in 1768 called it a *'paper mill ... brick stone and tiled not exceeding £400 ... Drying shed separate stone timber and tiled not exceeding £100'*. In 1770 when the mill was repaired before the lease from Thomas Houghton to Thomas Freeman, the repairs included

'The floor next the dam to be amended over the Cockle Room and six new treble sides to be provided. The water wheel to be well repaired with ten buckets and lined with lead. Also a new shuttle and a new bat and

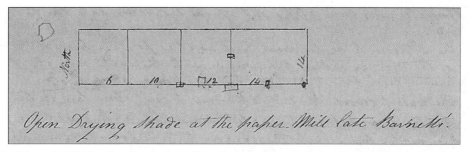

Fig. 7: Plan of 1837 for the conversion of the drying rooms at Lower Papermill into a tenement.
(courtesy of the Lincolnshire Archives Office and Mark Deyncourt)

tooth plate. New steps up to the engine and the stage round it to be amended. A new hood to the roll and the engine to be made to turn better. The flywheel to be new geared and the chimney belonging the cockle room to be amended. And further that he will allow the said Thomas Freeman four guineas for the repairs of the rag house (which he may convert into a dwelling house if he please) and also some stones for the same, after it shall be done'.

A cockle can mean a stove for drying paper. Cockle was also used to describe the edge of the paper which took the shape of the edge of a cockleshell when it dried; so the cockle room may refer to the room where the paper was pressed to remove the cockle edge. The 'treble sides' were the wooden bars that held the hessian in the drying lofts. The tooth plate was probably the device that lifted the hammers that beat the rags into pulp. In 1773 Thomas Freeman insured *'Spring Side Mill'* for £600. It consisted of the paper mill (£400) –*'brick stone and tile'* and a separate drying shed (£100) built of stone timber and tile. The utensils and stock were also insured (£100). In 1775, in addition to the property insured in 1773 there was also a *'house and drying house near said mill brick stone and covered with tarred paper'*. The original drying house was now partly tiled and partly thatched. So it seems that Thomas Freeman did convert the rag house into a dwelling. In 1792 it was described as *'all that paper mill with dwelling house drying houses and all other outbuildings thereto adjoining and belonging'*. The insurance policy taken out by Michael Gresham in 1794 called it *'the Lower Papermill, stone and tiled ... House only near in tenure of no hazardous trade stone and tiled ... and house adjoining not communicating used for drying paper thatched ... Warranted to have no stove or steam engine'*. A sales advertisement in 1799 described it as a *'capital freehold paper mill, standing at Tealby, with vats, presses etc., now in full employ'*. When Christopher

Dinsdale insured the property in 1802, the policy showed it as a *'water paper mill house containing one stove but no steam engine, brick built and tiled'*.

In 1837 Charles Tennyson d'Eyncourt had plans drawn up to show the conversion of the *'open drying shade at the paper mill late Barnett's'* into a tenement. The building was fourteen by forty-two feet and aligned north-south. The *'whole of the building to be walled round with a good common stone upon the present wall within the lattice work except where the windows are to be placed and drawn over twice with good lime mortar'*. The floors were to be made with dressed bricks laid on sand. The plans (Fig. 7) showed that the building was to be divided into four rooms.

The plans also show the conversion of the 'Saul Rooms', which were to the west of the mill, into two tenements. Each tenement had two rooms downstairs and two chambers (bedrooms) reached by a ladder. 'Saul Room' may have been a derivation of *'salle'* (French for room), which was used to describe a finishing room where women usually graded, sorted, counted, glazed and packed the paper. When the former paper mill at Lyng in Norfolk was advertised for sale in 1868, the catalogue included the following: - *'Old Sol Drying House'*, *'Sol Loft'* and *'Stove Room'*. The last two contained many rope lines and the stove room had a cast iron stove with 33 feet of six inch diameter pipe fitted with guards and stands. These were presumably used to dry the paper.

The Saul Rooms at Springside Papermill were twenty feet six inches by twenty-eight feet six inches and aligned east-west (Figs 8 & 9). The east-end joined to the mill through an archway, *'The inside walls and chimneys all to be taken down as well as the brick floor to be taken up. ... the two kitchens are to be the whole length of the North side ... four feet to be taken off each kitchen for two pantrys, ... the chimneys to be placed back to back ...*

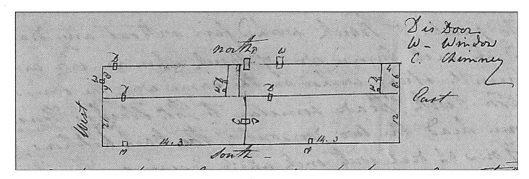

Fig. 8:

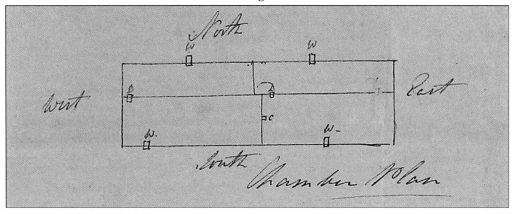

Figs. 8 and 9: Plans of 1837 for the conversion of the ground floor (Saul room) and first floor (rag chamber) of Lower Papermill into two tenements. (courtesy of the Lincolnshire Archives Office and Mark Deyncourt)

with openings sufficiently wide to admit a common sized oven, boiler and grate. ... The archway into the mill, to wall not in the centre of the arch but on the tenement side so as to leave the arch wholly in the inside of the mill, and the doorway into the rag chamber to be walled up...'. It seems that there was a rag chamber over the Saul room. Before the conversion, Thomas Starkes was lodging in two rooms of the Saul Rooms. The estimated cost for the three tenements was £91[2].

At the time of the 1861 census, '*Dinsdals Mill*' was occupied by Edward Tyson and his wife, Mary and by Leonard Walker and his family. Both husbands were agricultural labourers.

In November 1943 the hillside above the mill site subsided and slipped down towards the stream and the old Papermill Cottage. At the time, the *Market Rasen Mail* reported that the subsidence had moved the water mains several feet and caused them to fracture and cut off the supply to Market Rasen for two days. The Chairman

Fig. 10: Springside (Lower) Papermill, Tealby

of the Water Company said that the water main had been fractured six times during the previous 40 years by the movement of the hillside. During the repairs the workers came across '*many of the foundations of the old Tealby paper mill and had to cut through them*'. The same

Fig. 11: The chimney at Lower Papermill in 2000

hillside subsided again in the 1990s. Substantial work had to be carried out to repair the road.

Some of the last occupants of the Papermill Cottage (Fig. 10) were Joe Taylor who was a jobbing gardener and his spinster sister Annie. They moved to Cow Hill, the lane off Caistor Lane in about 1950. The last occupant was Jim Campion, a chimney sweep.

There are still some remains of the mill and dwelling house. It is possible to identify the old course of the diverted (leat or slip) stream to the east of the mill. In 1992 Stewart Squires conducted a survey of the site. He made the following observations: -

'The building remains consist of the lower courses, part exposed and part buried, of much of the outside walls, in extent 9 metres by 7 metres, the long side orientated east west. Inside it, and offset to the west, is

Fig. 12: Remains of the waterwheel arch of Lower Papermill in 2000, with Rachel Grasham the four times great granddaughter of Michael Grasham

a full height chimney [Fig. 11] with fireplaces on both sides to two floors. To the east are further remains of a second fireplace with internal walls. The building has collapsed internally, and to the south and west, and much of the masonry is overgrown. The walls appear to have been of local limestone with red brick quoins, internal walls appear to have been of brick, and broken pantiles indicate that this was the form of roofing material.

The outside of the eastern wall falls to a lower level. The wall is of limestone rubble. Set into the outside face are brick courses in an arch of a maximum of 6-foot diameter, indicating the location and position of the water wheel [Fig. 12]. On the upstream side of this is a partially collapsed culvert, its invert level in relation to the wheel diameter indicating that the wheel was breast-shot.

East of wheel pit are the foundations of two further walls, their purpose as yet not clear, although the first may indicate the east wall of the Mill, and the second the wall of a leat serving the culvert, where there may have been a sluice.

Further to the north-east and south-west the enclosure of the site is indicated. That to the north east consists of partially buried overgrown wall bases, including the base of a gatepost. To the west is a section of overgrown, once plashed, hawthorn hedging.

The north western corner of the enclosure is identified by the remnants of a small stone walled building, remains of the two outside walls still standing to a height of 2 metres. The base of the wall is indicated by overgrown footings, and the building appears to have collapsed inwards, internally the floor level being well raised, rough and overgrown. This building may have been a drying shed or rag store.

To the south of the mill the river falls over a small weir with a drop of about 0.7 of a metre. To the north and south of the mill site the river is contained in a narrow steep sided valley. By the mill the valley widens and flattens. This feature, natural or otherwise, and the weir, may well indicate the site of a former millpond. Present day water levels are lower than those of the last century as water is abstracted and stored now direct from the Bully Hill springs further up the valley'.

The owners and occupiers of Springside (Lower) Papermill were: -

Date	Owner	Occupier/Tenant
1748	Henry Boulton	
1763	Hinman Allenby	Thomas Houghton

1768	Thomas Houghton	Thomas Houghton
1770	Thomas Houghton	Thomas Freeman
1773	Thomas Freeman	Thomas Freeman
1792	Michael Gresham	Michael Gresham
1799	Christopher Dinsdale	Christopher Dinsdale
1832	Christopher Dinsdale's trustees	Hercules Barnett
1834	Hercules Barnett	Hercules Barnett
1835	Hercules Barnett (now living in Hull)	?
1837	Charles Tennyson d'Eyncourt	?

The Papermill or Whitehead's Mill

The third mill was just known as 'The Papermill' and was built by Edward Whitehead in 1800 on the site of a former fulling mill; he purchased the site from the creditors of Michael Gresham for £106. It was about 500 yards to the east of Tealby Church (N.G.R. TF 161908) at a fifteen-

Figs 13a & 13b: The waterfall at Whitehead's Mill as it looked in 1905 and as it appeared in 2001. The stone sill at the top can just be seen in the modern photograph

Fig. 14: The brick mill intake and the sill of Whitehead's Mill in 2001

feet high waterfall (Fig. 13a). The natural course of the stream has been diverted in order to provide a millpond and sufficient fall over the waterfall to give power to the waterwheel. A false stream like this is known as a leat or slipstream. This mill was number 205 in the 1816 Excise Lists. In 1839 the property consisted of *'a freehold and commodious mill situate upon a powerful stream of water, and drying lofts, drying shades, store rooms, rag-house, stove room, barn stables and wagon- house, besides two cottages for the occupation of workmen. Adjoining the mill is a messuage in which the proprietor at present resides.'* The dwelling house was built of brick and stone and had a tiled roof when Edward Whitehead insured it in 1831. At the time of the 1861 census, 'Whiteheads Mill' was shown as two unoccupied properties.

When Stewart Squires surveyed the site in 1992 he made the following comments: -

'At the time of the taking in of this area into Bayons Manor Park, the opportunity was taken to utilise the fall which drove the mill to create a spectacular 4.5 metre waterfall. To complement this a grove of trees was planted around it. Contemporary photographs show it to have been a picturesque spot. Large blocks of Tealby limestone were used for the back and the sides to give a natural look.

Water no longer passes over the fall and the river has been diverted back to its lower natural course nearby. Leading upriver from the site is a leat built as a shelf on the valley side for a distance of about 110 metres, where a sluice survives. The sluice and its brickwork are of the late C19, but the wing walls are of earlier brick, similar to that used to build Lower Mill in

the late C18, indicating the site of a sluice used in connection with the former mill.

At the head of the fall the river has been channelled through a brick walled trough, and at the base of the fall is an overgrown brick chamber. These are of late C19 bricks contemporary with those at the sluice. They appear to be consistent with an agricultural use most probably for dipping sheep.'

In 2001 it was still possible to see the remains of the brick millrace, however there is only a slight trickle of water going over the falls (Fig. 13b) and the gateway access from Papermill Lane is still present. All that now remains of the mill is the silted up millpond with a sluice gate about one hundred yards to the east of the site, the brick intake, the sill (Fig. 14), the waterfall and some minor brickwork at the base of the falls. The sluice and the brickwork at the base of the falls may be part of the system used in the 1930s to extract water for Market Rasen rather than the purposes suggested by Stewart Squires.

The owners and occupiers of this mill were: -

Date	Owner	Occupier/Tenant
1768	Edward Chapman	Fulling Mill
1790	Thomas Freeman	Fulling Mill
1792	Michael Gresham	Michael Gresham (site of mill only)
1800	Edward Whitehead	Edward Whitehead
1826	Edward Whitehead	William Smith
1829	Edward Whitehead	Edward Smith
1840	Charles Tennyson d'Eyncourt	Charles Tennyson d'Eyncourt

Papermaking ended in Tealby between 1829 and 1835 due the increased competition from machine-made paper using the new Fourdrinier machine, as well as due to the difficulties in importing the raw material. In January 1800 the price of paper rose by 10% due to difficulties of importing rags from Europe because of the political turmoil caused by Napoleon. The stationers were afraid that many printing businesses would have to stop work. They had a meeting with the Prime Minister, William Pitt, to try to persuade him to arrange a large quantity of rags. In January 1805 writing and printing paper prices rose by 17% and brown papers by 7½%. Another reason for the decline in papermaking was that excise taxes were levied on all paper.

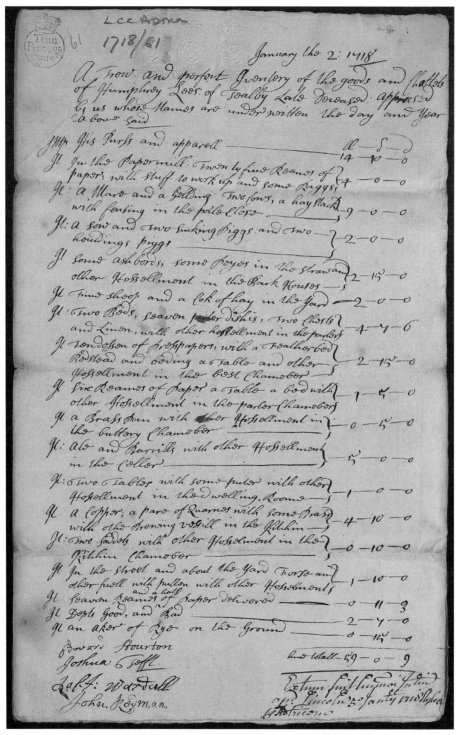

Fig. 15: The inventory of Humphrey Lees's possessions made five days after his death on 28 December 1718
(courtesy Lincolnshire Archives Office and the Diocese of Lincoln)

Tealby Papermaking Families

Humphrey Lees (? - 1718)

Humphrey Lees married Sarah Harnisse (sic) at Tealby on 7 February 1689; she was possibly the widow of Thomas Harnesse (sic). Humphrey and Sarah had one child, also Humphrey, who was baptised at Tealby on 15 May 1692; he died aged one year. Sarah had had four children with Thomas: - Elizabeth (1675), Sarah (1680), William (1685) and Thomas (1685).

Humphrey Lees died in Tealby on 28 December 1718 and an inventory was taken of his possessions five days later[3] (Fig. 15). He was the earliest known papermaker in Tealby. Edward Stourton, John Rodman, Joshua Teffe and Robert Wardell all witnessed the inventory. Joshua Teffe was a farmer and the brother in law of Edward Stourton. Humphrey did not leave any real estate so he was probably the tenant of the Edward Stourton at the Top Papermill. The inventory included *'In the paper mill twenty five reames of paper with stuff to work up and some rags ... £4 ... ten dossens of presspapers ... in the best chamber ... six reames of paper in the parlor chamber …[and] seven reames and a half of paper delivered ... 11s 3d'*. The house consisted of the following rooms:- parlour, dwelling room, kitchen, cellar, best chamber, parlour chamber, buttery chamber, kitchen chamber. There were beds in the best chamber (one), parlour chamber (one) and in the parlour (two), but none in any of the other chambers. They may have been only attic spaces. The total value of his possessions was £59 0s 9d. Presumably the seven and a half reams shown as delivered had been dispatched but not yet paid for.

Humphrey died intestate and administration was granted to his widow Sara (sic). Robert Harniss and William Stamp also signed the administration papers; they were both farmers from Tealby. Robert was Sarah's nephew and he took over the tenancy of the paper mill.

Robert Harness (1668-1721) and Thomas Harness (1703-1776)

Robert Harness was the son of William and Elizabeth (nee Wright) and was baptised in Tealby on 28 October 1668. William was a butcher in Caistor in 1672. Robert was four years old in 1672 when he became the beneficiary of the estate of his uncle, Robert Harness, who was a butcher in Tealby and married to Elizabeth (nee

Bagley). The inventory of Robert's possessions included two houses, 85 acres of land (probably copyhold), eight draught oxen, eight cows and over 200 sheep. The total value of the estate was £210. Robert (jnr) married Elizabeth Routh at Tealby on 1 May 1701 and they had three children: Thomas (1703), Robert (1705) and William (1707). Robert was the step-nephew of Humphrey Lees the papermaker and took over the lease on Top Papermill when Humphrey died in 1718. At that time Robert was described as a farmer. Robert agreed to take John Laming as an apprentice papermaker for nine years from 1 June 1721[4]. John was thirteen and the son of Marmaduke Laming, a chair-maker from Market Rasen. Robert died six months later aged 53 and was buried on 9 December 1721; he was described as a papermaker from Tealby on his *'true and perfect inventory of all the goods and chattels'*[5](Fig. 16). The inventory included the following items: -

a leas of paper miln;	£50
in ye miln paper and raggs;	£35
in ye paper house ready paper;	£9
in ye paper house pack sheets; sadles with other utensils	£2
five horses;	£15

The house consisted of a hall, a parlour, a dairy, a cellar, a kitchen and two bedrooms. There were five beds. The description of the house is very similar to the house occupied by Humphrey Lees. There were also about 100 sheep and four cows in various fields. The total value was £295, which was quite a considerable sum. It was equivalent to over five years' wages for one of his employees. The witnesses were Edward Stourton (1680-1753) who was probably his landlord and Robert Bagley, his brother-in-law.

Robert's oldest son, Thomas, married Elizabeth Brooks at Tealby on 23 November 1724. Elizabeth was the daughter of Thomas Brooks, a miller in Tealby. In Thomas Harness's marriage settlement (dated 17 November 1724) he was described as a papermaker from Tealby; he conveyed a jointure for her maintenance and support if she outlived him. It consisted of *'all that messuage cotage situate in Tealby with croft with one acre'* plus several selions of land in the common fields.

It is presumed that Thomas took over the lease on the paper mill when he was eighteen years old when his

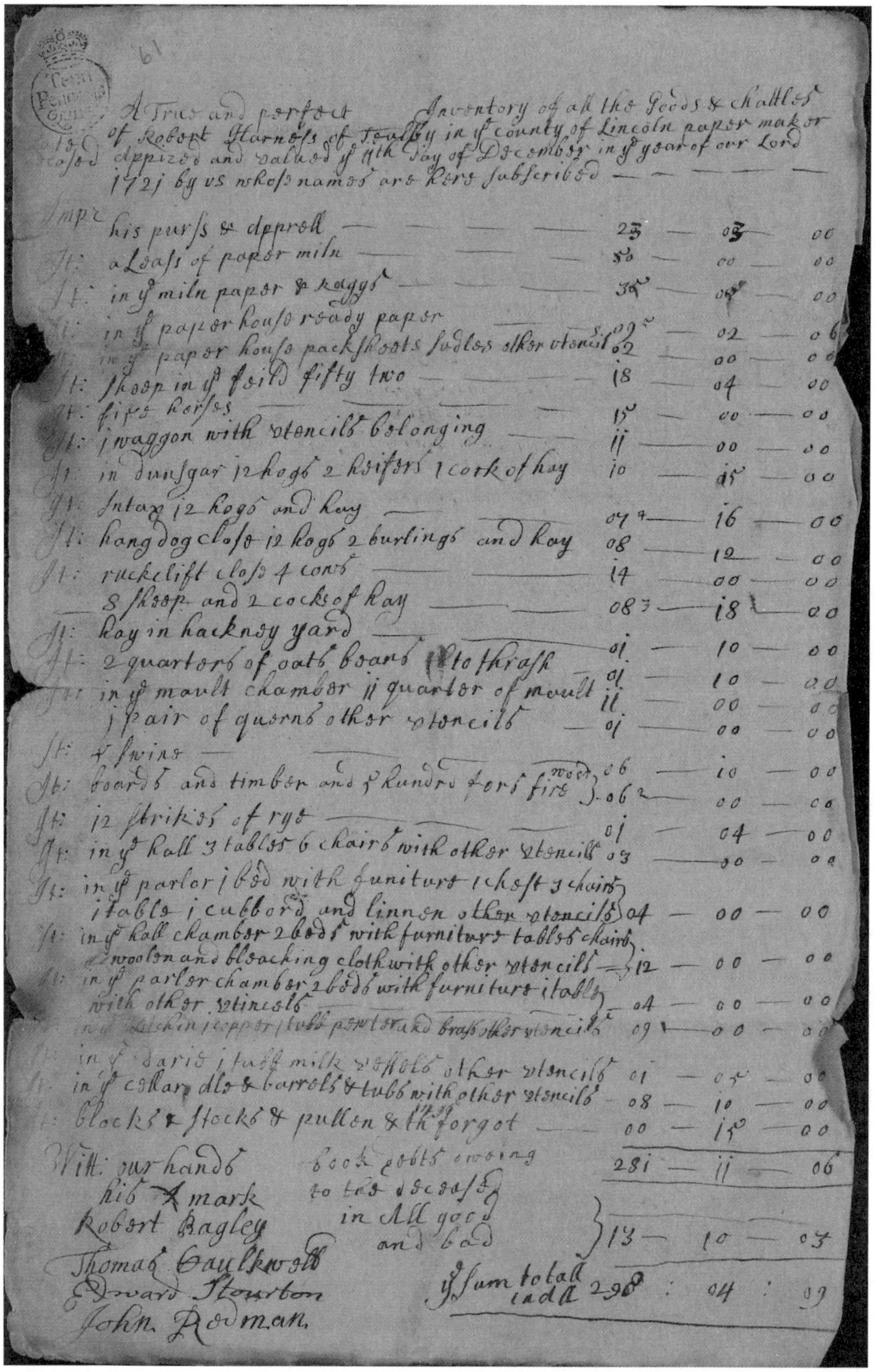

A True and perfect Inventory of all the Goods & chattles of Robert Harness of Tealby in ye county of Lincoln paper maker deceased apprized and valued ye 11th day of December in ye year of our Lord 1721 by us whose names are here subscribed

Impr	his purs & apprell	23	03	00
It:	a Lease of paper miln	80	00	00
It:	in ye miln paper & raggs	39	04	00
It:	in ye paper house ready paper	09	02	06
	in ye paper house packsheets sadles other utensils	02	00	00
It:	sheep in ye feild fifty two	18	04	00
It:	five horses	15	00	00
It:	1 waggon with utensils belonging	11	00	00
It:	in dunsgar 12 hogs 2 heifers 1 cock of hay	10	15	00
It:	Intax 12 hogs and hay	07	16	00
It:	hang dog close 12 hogs 2 burlings and hay	08	12	00
It:	ruckclift close 4 cows	14	00	00
	8 sheep and 2 cocks of hay	08	18	00
It:	hay in hackney yard	01	10	00
It:	2 quarters of oats beans to thrash	01	10	00
It:	in ye moult chamber 11 quarter of moult	11	00	00
	1 pair of querns other utensils	01	00	00
It:	4 swine	06	10	00
It:	boards and timber and ye hundred fore fire wood	06	00	00
It:	12 strikes of rye	01	04	00
It:	in ye hall 3 tables 6 chairs with other utensils	03	00	00
It:	in ye parlor 1 bed with funiture 1 chest 3 chairs 1 table 1 cubbord and linnen other utensils	04	00	00
It:	in ye hall chamber 2 beds with furniture tables chairs woolen and bleaching cloth with other utensils	12	00	00
It:	in ye parlor chamber 2 beds with furniture 1 table with other utensils	04	00	00
	in ye kitchin 1 copper 1 tubb pewter and brass other utensils	09	00	00
	in ye dairie 1 tubb milk vessels other utensils	01	05	00
It:	in ye cellar ale & barrels & tubbs with other utensils	08	10	00
It:	blocks & stocks & pullen & things forgot	00	15	00
		281	11	06
	book debts owing to the deceased in All good and bad	13	10	03
	ye sum total is	295	04	09

Witt: our hands
his X mark
Robert Bagley
Thomas Faulkworth
Edward Stourton
John Redman

Fig. 16: The 'true and perfect inventory of all the goods and chattels' of papermaker Robert Harness who died in December 1721 (courtesy Lincolnshire Archives Office and the Diocese of Lincoln)

father died in 1721 and probably took on John Laming, his father's apprentice. The Lincolnshire Archives have an invoice[6] from Thomas Harniss to Mr Cla[y]ton for 4½ reams of paper supplied between 1743 and 1749. There were two sizes of paper, '*H Pott*' (about A3 size) at 10/- a ream and '*H ... Cap*' (possibly foolscap) at 14/- a ream. A ream (=20 quires or 480 sheets) cost about the same as the weekly wage of a farm labourer, so it was relatively very expensive when compared to the price today. The bill was settled in 1756! Thomas took on a sixteen-year-old apprentice called James Nutt in 1750.

The mill lease was taken over by Thomas Houghton in 1763 and Thomas Harness (senior) was buried at Tealby on 24 January 1776, aged 72. James Nutt (his former apprentice) was buried in Tealby on 25 April 1820 aged 86.

William Hemsworth

William Hemsworth was probably born in Ordsall, Retford, in 1704. He married Mary Richardson at Worksop, which is about seven miles from Retford, on 19 December 1731. Shorter[7] reported that William was a master papermaker at Springside Mill in 1731. It is considered that he was more likely a tenant of Edward Stourton at High Papermill. William had two children born in 1740 and 1743 at Ordsall. This indicates that William and Mary moved back to Ordsall sometime between 1731 and 1740.

The Stourton Family

The earliest Stourton connection in the Tealby area was Erasmus Stourton in 1631; he was born in Narborough, Leicestershire in 1603 and was the son of Edward and Mary (nee Sanderson) Stourton. Mary was the widow of William Beck of Narborough. Erasmus studied theology at St John's College, Cambridge where he was exposed to the latest Puritan teachings and took his BA in 1622-23 and his MA in 1627. He was ordained a deacon and became a priest at Peterborough in 1625.

Erasmus went to Newfoundland with the early settlers. Newfoundland had been claimed for Queen Elizabeth in 1583 and Stourton was one of the first Church of England clergymen on the island serving at Ferryland (about 30 miles south of St John's) in 1627 to 1628. At the time of 'Militant Protestantism', Stourton was known as the 'Puritan Minister' in the colony. In 1627 Lord Baltimore

(formerly, George Calvert) arrived in the island to oversee his newly purchased lands. He had been one of the principal Secretaries of State and had been knighted by James I. He had converted to Catholicism and took two priests with him to Newfoundland. The priests offered the first mass in British North America at Ferryland and they also forced the baptism of a Protestant child according to the customs of the Church of Rome, a practice considered objectionable, if not treasonable. Erasmus Stourton made it his business to investigate the rumours of 'Popish practices'. There followed an acrimonious meeting with Lord Baltimore who used the powers of his charter and Stourton was banished from the island. On his return to Plymouth on 28 August 1628, he complained to his Puritan associates about the encouragement of Catholicism, but because of Baltimore's reputation for liberality and enlightenment, no action was taken.

Erasmus Stourton became chaplain to Christopher Villiers, Lord of Anglesey, brother of George Villiers who had been created the 1st Duke of Buckingham in 1623. George Villiers was one of the homosexual favourites of James I. Buckingham was given a lot of land and he became the richest nobleman in England. A discontented army officer in Portsmouth murdered him in 1628 after an unsuccessful expedition against France. In 1628 Erasmus married Elizabeth Gravenor at Bellaport, Cheshire, and their first child, Edward, was baptised at Spalding in 1629. This suggests that Erasmus was given a living in Spalding. Following the forced resignation of Robert Burton of Walesby in 1631 he was presented with the rectorship by Lionel Cranfield, the Earl of Middlesex, who was related by marriage to Christopher Villiers and to the Duke of Buckingham. Stourton held the rectorship until his death in 1658. Erasmus and Elizabeth had five children, all baptised at Walesby.

When Erasmus died, his son Thomas succeeded him as rector. Thomas had studied at Trinity College, Cambridge, and had taken his BA in 1656-57. Elizabeth wrote her last will in 1670 when she lived at Risby. She left Thomas the '*linnen at present in his possession, study of books, locke cupboards, the bed and furniture to it belong which stood in the middle chamber of his house and one brass pot*'. She also left him '*£26 owing from him to me and a mourning ring*'. In addition, she left a mourning ring to her oldest son Edward, the remaining goods and chattels were to be appraised sold and the proceeds divided between her two youngest children, Matthew and Frances. Thomas died in May 1677 at the age of 32. He left a widow and six

Fig. 17: The signature of Edward Stourton the Elder (courtesy Lincolnshire Archives Office and Mark Deyncourt)

children under the age of eleven. When he wrote his will in October 1676 he was described as '*very infirm*' and he wished to be buried in the chancel of Walesby Church. He left £5 to each of his children when they reached the age of 21. The residue was left to his widow Anne. The inventory of his possessions was valued at £259. There was no property included in the list, but there were four oxen, eight cows and a bull, thirteen young beasts, seven weaning calves, 80 sheep and 40 lambs, two mares, one foal and one colt. There was an Anne Stourton, a widow, buried at Wragby in 1721. She was possibly Thomas's widow. She left twenty guineas to her son who was an ironmonger in the City of London.

Edward was the eldest son of Erasmus and Elizabeth; he was born in 1629 and he studied at St John's College, Cambridge. He took his BA in 1649 to 1650; his MA in 1653 and he became licensed to practice medicine in 1654. He married Jane Perkins in Spalding in 1658. She was the daughter of William Slater of Spalding and the widow of Wyatt Perkins. They did not have any children. He became an MD in 1660 and he was also a Justice of the Peace for Lincolnshire. His last will was written on 8 August 1680 where he described himself as a '*Doctor of Phisick*' and that he was '*sick in body*'. He left his sister Frances an income of £20 a year from his freehold properties. He also left his freehold lands in Sutterton and Fleet Weston to Edward (aged fourteen), the eldest son of his deceased brother Thomas (Rector of Walesby). If Edward left no heirs then the property passed to Edward's brothers Thomas, John and Matthew, in turn. He assigned his leasehold properties in Spalding and Pinchbeck to trustees for the benefit of the children of his deceased brother Thomas. The trustees were to pay '*such sum, as they think necessary for their education and bringing up*'. He left his brother, Matthew, '*messuages, cottages and lands in Moulton and Holbeck, held by leases from ye late Queen Henrietta Maria, and also all copyhold land in Pinchbeck*'. Queen Henrietta Maria was the wife of

Charles I. The trustees were to be guardians to his nephew Edward and executors in trust for all the children of his brothers Thomas and Matthew. Edward had obviously been very successful during his life.

Matthew, the fourth son of Erasmus and Elizabeth, was born in Walesby in 1636 and he became a farmer and yeoman in Tealby. He married Catherine Huddleston on 2 February 1674 at Waddingham. It seems highly probable that Matthew and Elizabeth brought up the six children of Matthew's brother Thomas, who died in 1677 at the age of 32. At that time Matthew and Catherine had two young children, Erasmus (b.1675) and Dorothy (b.1676) and they subsequently had five more - Edward 'the elder'(b.1680), George (b.1684), Elizabeth (b.1688), John (b.1695) and Catherine, so they probably looked after thirteen children. Matthew (senior) wrote his last will and died in 1701 and he left a cottage and four closes to Catherine for her lifetime '*in lieu of her dower and thirds*'. 'Thirds' means the third part of a deceased husband's personal property to which the widow was entitled. After Catherine's death the property was to be equally shared by Matthew's sons Edward and Matthew. Matthew, his 'son' was actually the son of his deceased brother Thomas. Matthew also left ten shillings to his daughter Dorothy and £60 apiece to his children Catherine, George, Elizabeth, Erasmus and John. He also left his messuage and remaining lands to be equally shared by his 'sons' Edward and Matthew.

Matthew the fourth son of Thomas and Anne took his BA at Magdalene College Cambridge in 1694-95. He was ordained as a deacon at Lincoln in 1698 and married Alice Short in Market Rasen in 1713. They had seven children, all baptised in Tealby. Matthew must have given up his church living because he was later described as a grazier and farmer in Tealby. He died in 1737 leaving his half share to his son Matthew. In 1746 there was an agreement between Edward (the elder) and Matthew his nephew to finally agree the division of property they had inherited

Fig. 18: The signature of Edward Stourton (the younger) (courtesy Lincolnshire Archives Office and Mark Deyncourt)

from Edward's father (Matthew) and '*for putting an end to all disputes and controversies which have arisen between them*'. In addition, John, who died in 1754, refers to his brother Matthew in his will. The disputes were probably due to family rivalry, possibly caused by the families of Thomas (1634-1677) and Matthew (1636-1700) being brought up together.

Edward Stourton the Elder (1680-1753) was the son of Matthew and Catherine Stourton of Tealby and the nephew of Thomas Stourton (1634-1677) the Rector of Walesby. Edward was a grazier, farmer and yeoman farmer in Tealby, who married Ann Teffe at Tealby in 1710. Ann was the daughter of Samuel and Mary Teffe. Samuel was yeoman farmer in Tealby.

Edward Stourton was one of the witnesses to the inventories of Humphrey Lees (1718) (Fig. 15) and of Robert Harness (1721) (Fig. 16), papermakers in Tealby. He was probably their landlord. In the agreement signed by Edward (the elder) and his nephew Matthew in 1746, one of the pieces of land was described as '*three leys near Edward Stourton's paper mill*'. This was Pad Mill (or High Papermill). Edward the elder owned it but Edward the younger occupied it. Shorter[8] stated that Edward Stourton, papermaker, insured his paper mill with Sun Fire Insurance[9] in 1740. This is a mistake; John Temple took out this policy on a watermill in Thornay in Norfolk. In 1751 Mary Camm, a widow from Lincoln, signed a lease with Edward Stourton, the younger, papermaker of Tealby for '*2 cottages now much decayed in the occupation of Thomas Clarke and William Stretton and one close lying near the fulling mill of Thomas Noel*'. On 4 May 1752 Edward the elder signed a one year lease on '*all that new erected messuage or tenement and paper mill thereto adjoining now called the Papermill or Pad Mill*' and about 130 acres to Revd John Teffe, his brother-in-law, the Rector of Croxby. Edward, the elder, died in 1753; his grave is a large stone tomb on the south side of

Tealby Church. He left most of his property to his eldest son Edward (the younger), papermaker and merchant. In 1753 Edward (the younger) signed an agreement with his cousin Matthew in which Matthew agreed to specify the title to Edward for the various properties. This was presumably a continuation of the family disputes.

Edward Stourton (the younger) '*of Tealby*' married Elizabeth Thorold '*of Louth*' by licence at Keddington, Louth on 6 May 1752. She was the daughter of Thomas Thorold, a miller and baker, from Louth. The date of the wedding coincides with the agreement by Edward's father to lease the paper mill in Tealby for one year. In 1754 Edward was described as a papermaker from Tealby when his father-in-law assigned the lease of a corn mill, oat kiln and drying house in Louth to him and William Thorold, Edward's brother-in-law. On 3 July 1755 Edward Stouerton (sic) of Louth, papermaker, took out insurance with Sun Fire (Fig. 5)[10] on his paper mill in Tilby (sic). The Simmons Collection[11] states that Edward Stourton was from Thorpe Hall Mill in Louth. This is presumably an error as there was no mention of Thorpe Hall Mill in the insurance policy. The mill that was insured was High Papermill (or Pad Mill) in Tealby and consisted of the mill with drying rooms warerooms and offices adjoining, built with stone, brick, timber, tiles and thatched. It was '*in his own occupation*' and valued at £160. The utensils and stock were valued at a further £40. It seems probable that Edward Stourton was living in Louth in 1755 but was not a papermaker in Louth. The Louth paper mill was described as newly built in 1798, so it is unlikely that it was there in 1755.

Edward and Elizabeth did not have any children and Edward wrote his last will on 24 January 1756 and he described himself as '*indisposed in body*' and as a paper merchant from Louth. He was buried at Tealby just twelve days later, aged 45. He left his household goods and furniture at Louth to his widow, Elizabeth. Edward left his half share '*in the hearse and post chaise which I have with his brother William*' to his brother-in-law, Thomas Thorold. A post chaise was a light and comfortable vehicle with four wheels and drawn by two or four horses ridden by post boys. The horses were changed at regular stations. It seems that Edward had a business with his brother-in-law in which they hired out the hearse and post chaise. Edward also left £100 each to his nephews Edward and Thomas Carr and '*to each of my labourers and working people of Tealby one week's wages*'. He left the residue of his estate (which included the paper mill at Tealby) in equal shares to his two surviving brothers, John and Matthew. They had to pay Edward's widow an annuity of £28 a year in lieu of her 'dower and thirds'. There was an Elizabeth Stourton (77) of Louth buried at Tealby on 21 August 1816. She was probably the widow of Edward the younger. If the age was correct, she was born in 1739 and was only thirteen when she married.

When Matthew (the brother of Edward the younger) wrote his last will in 1786 he described himself as a '*gentleman*' living in New Road, St Pancras in the Fields, Middlesex. He was '*weak in body, but sound of mind memory and understanding*'. He had previously been a baker at Drury Lane, St Giles in the Fields, Middlesex, having inherited the bakery business from his Uncle John in 1754. According to the Tealby Land Tax assessments for 1791 John Stourton was an owner/occupier and paying £4 15s 4d in tax and Matthew Stourton as owner paying £2 10s 8d tax. The occupier was Thomas Moody. On 12 May 1791 John '*a gentleman from North Willingham*' and Matthew '*a gentleman from Totteringham* [sic] *Court Road, Westminster*' let the paper mill to Michael Gresham for fifteen years at £60 a year (the agreement was signed in 1790). John died in 1791 and Matthew died in 1792 leaving their half shares to their respective sons - Edward and Joseph Huddleston Stourton. Joseph's share was left in trust with his cousin Edward Carr and his mother Mary until he reached the age of 21 (i.e. in 1787). Probate was not granted on Matthew's estate until 3 June 1797. Mary died in 1799 and the property then passed to Joseph. Matthew must have been a wealthy man because he left sixteen London properties as well as the Tealby property. The Tealby Land Tax for 1792 shows that most of the land previously owned by Matthew was owned by George Tennyson, and Edward Stourton occupied John Stourton's land. Before enclosure, Edward owned about fifteen acres in his own right and shared eight more acres (including High Papermill) with Joseph. At the enclosure,

Edward was allotted three more acres and Edward and Joseph were allotted an extra 132 acres. After enclosure they were the fourth largest landowners in the village. In 1798 Michael Gresham became bankrupt and John Clarke took over the tenancy in 1799 for £15 a year until 1806. The following year Joseph sold his half share of the mill, about ten acres and a newly erected farmhouse tenanted by his cousin Edward Stourton to George Tennyson for £1,354. Edward Stourton moved to North Willingham and sold his half share of the mill and about 200 acres to George Tennyson in 1802 for £1,700. Edward moved to Barrow on Humber and then to Laceby where he died in 1824. Edward described himself as a '*gentleman*' from 1802, so he was presumably living on the income from his sale to George Tennyson. His oldest son John Beck Stourton farmed at Cabourn and died in 1856

Alice Stourton, a great granddaughter of Thomas Stourton the Rector of Walesby and second cousin once removed from Edward Stourton the younger married Christopher Dinsdale. He purchased Lower Papermill in 1800 and operated it until 1832. Alice had five children and she died in 1814.

Thomas Houghton

Thomas Houghton, the son of Thomas and Elizabeth Houghton, was baptised at Wrawby near Brigg on 26 February 1737 (or 1738). He married Sarah Hickson at Holy Trinity Church, Hull, on 18 August 1756 and they had a son, also Thomas, who was baptised in Tealby on 4 March 1759. Sarah died on 9 September 1800, aged 66, and her gravestone is in Tealby Churchyard at the eastern end of the Church. Thomas took over the estate of John Foston. Thomas senior may have been the person who, in 1768, was described as a papermaker from Market Rasen when he purchased the following from Mr Hinman Allenby of Maidenwell: 77 acres in the open fields; six acres of pasture; four beast gates and '*all that water mill now used as a paper mill together with the little Pingle* [i.e. a small piece of enclosed land] *thereto adjoining ... now in the tenure of the said Thomas Houghton*'. Also included in the transaction were the following pieces of land: - Little Bardill; Bull Cock Yard; Home Yard; Catskin Close and Barnapit Close with a total of almost seven acres. The total cost was £770. Thomas Houghton insured Springside Papermill and its contents in 1768 with Sun Fire Insurance[12] for £600. In 1770, when he leased a paper mill at Tealby to Thomas Freeman, Thomas

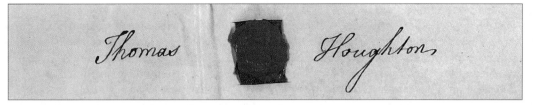

Fig. 19: The signature of Thomas Houghton (courtesy Lincolnshire Archives Office and Mark Deyncourt)

Houghton was described as a papermaker from Tealby; he also held a paper mill belonging to John Stourton. In 1771 Thomas Houghton was a draper in Market Rasen when he sold 66 acres of arable land and four beast gates to John Ling, a saddler from Market Rasen, for £465. By 1772 when he sold the mill and seven acres to Thomas Freeman for £430, he was a mercer, draper and grocer. In 1773 he sold a further seven acres and a messuage to Freeman for £370. In 1780, Thomas Houghton was described as a papermaker from Market Rasen when he insured[13] his paper mill at Barrow on Humber which was in the tenure of Thomas Houghton (his son?). Thomas Houghton the elder and younger, papermakers, dealers and chapmen (traders) were both reported as bankrupt at Wilminton Mill, Sutton-in-Holderness, Yorkshire in 1788[14]. According to the administration of Thomas's estate[15], in 1827 he '*departed this life many years ago*', intestate. The value of his estate was reported as less than £20. There is some confusion about which reports refer to the father or son. It seems likely that Thomas Houghton the elder stopped being a papermaker at Tealby in 1771, but his son continued at Barrow on Humber and at Sutton-in-Holderness between 1780 and 1788. Thomas junior returned to live in Barrow on Humber sometime before 1793. A Thomas Houghton married Ann Crowder at Barton-upon-Humber in 1794. He was probably the same Thomas Houghton who was the papermaker and they had three children baptised at South Ferriby. They were Mary (1798), Elizabeth (1803) and Thomas (1805). It is not known what happened to the family after 1805.

Thomas Freeman (The Younger) (1745-?)

Thomas Freeman was the son of Thomas Freeman and was baptised in Tamworth, Staffordshire on 2 July 1745. He married Alice Hubbard at Lichfield on 21 June 1770. Thomas Freeman the younger was described as a papermaker from Tamworth when he leased a paper mill from Thomas Houghton in March 1770. He agreed to lease the mill for 21 years at £25 a year from '*old Mayday*'. The mill must have been in a poor state of repair because Thomas Houghton agreed to repair the mill before the lease commenced. The repairs included:

'*The floor next the dam to be amended over the Cockle Room and six new treble sides to be provided. The water wheel to be well repaired with ten buckets and lined with lead. Also a new shuttle a new bat and tooth plate. New steps up to the engine and the stage round it to be amended. A new hood to the roll and the engine to be made to turn better. The flywheel to be new geared and the chimney belonging the cockle room to be amended. And further that he will allow the said Thomas Freeman four guineas for the repairs of the rag house (which he may convert into a dwelling house if he please) and also some stones for the same, after it shall be done*'.

Freeman had an option to buy the mill for £450 during the first seven years of the lease. He also agreed to purchase all the rags and utensils at the mill and also those at the mill that Houghton leased from John Stourton for a price to be mutually agreed at a later date.

Fig. 20: The signature of Thomas Freeman (courtesy Lincolnshire Archives Office and Mark Deyncourt)

Thomas and Alice Freeman had a son, Thomas Alexander who was baptised at Tealby on 19 January 1772. In 1772 Thomas Freeman purchased the mill for £430 from Thomas Houghton who was, by then, a mercer, draper and grocer in Market Rasen. Freeman took out a mortgage for £300 from a Mr Richard Read of Tathwell. Thomas insured Springside Papermill with Sun Fire Insurance[16] on 30 December 1772. He took out another insurance policy on 13 September 1775[17]. This time there was an additional drying house. The policy was endorsed in favour of Richard Read, the mortgagor. In 1773 Thomas Freeman purchased a further seven acres from Thomas Houghton for £370. In 1790 Thomas also bought a fulling mill from Robert Chapman. Thomas Freeman continued as a papermaker until October 1792 when he agreed to sell the mill and other property to Michael Gresham for £1,800. The property included a mill site where the fulling mill had been situated. The

Fig. 21: 'Freemans' now called Tealby Vale (early 1900s)

Fig. 22: Tealby Vale from the south (in 2003)

mortgage was then assigned to Michael Gresham. In 1791 Thomas Freeman was a tenant of Robert Manners (one of the Lords of the Manor of Tealby) and was paying £3 17s in Land Tax. He was also an owner/occupier and paying £1 5s 6d on two properties. Thomas Freeman lived at what is now Tealby Vale in Caistor Lane until 1792 (Figs 21 & 22). After the 1792 to 1795 enclosure, Thomas Freeman owned about three acres containing a homestead and a yard, which were situated near Asholt in Bayons Park. He was allotted a further five and a half acres in Jennyhole Field opposite the southern end of Thorpe Lane. Thomas Freeman was an owner of property with Thomas Dent as the occupier and paying Land Tax between 1792 and 1820.

Thomas Freeman also leased a paper mill at Barrow on Humber prior to the enclosure in 1803. He probably moved from Tealby in 1792 and Francis Gunnell also moved from Tealby to Barrow on Humber at the same time to become a papermaker for Thomas Freeman. Alice Freeman was a widow from Tamworth when she wrote her last will in 1826.

Michael Gresham (1739-1815?)
(Gresham is variously signed and spelt Grasham, Grassham or Grassam)

Michael Gresham was the son of John and Sarah Gresham (nee Reith) who were married on 17 August 1739 and Michael was baptised at Bishop Norton on 31 October 1739. When Michael Gresham married Elizabeth Bullivant at Tealby on 29 May 1766 they were both aged 27 and described as '*both of this parish*' and he signed himself as '*Michael Grassham*'. Elizabeth was the daughter of Thomas and Elizabeth (nee Brooks) Bullivant who were married at Tealby on 13 January 1736 and she was baptised at Tealby on 22 October 1738. Thomas Bullivant was a Methodist leader in the Grimsby Circuit in 1780. Michael and Elizabeth had four children baptised in Tealby. Michael was a member of the Tealby Society (Methodists) from 1769. He was a subscriber to build an 'Independent' house of worship according to the 'Dissenters Certificate' for 1780. This '*preaching house*' was situated in Caistor Lane, nearly opposite to Tealby Vale, where he later lived. The building was '*only used for the teachings of John Wesley*'.

In 1782 Michael was a tenant of Henry Martinson and paying £7 14s in Land Tax. In 1784 and 1785 he was described as a farmer on the Tealby Society register and he was the foreman of the jury of the Manor Court. By 1791 he was an owner/occupier and paying £1 5s 6d. In 1791 Michael took out a fifteen-year lease on '*a messuage* [a dwelling with outbuildings and associated land then used as several habitations] *with paper mill adjoining and 2 acres*' from John and Matthew Stourton for £60 a year. This was High or Top Papermill situated on the north side of the road at the bottom of Bully Hill.

On 10 October 1792 Michael purchased Springside paper mill and other property for £1,800 from Thomas Freeman and others. The property consisted of '*all that messuage or tenement wherein the said Thomas Freeman then dwelt with the barn stables dove cote granary and all other outbuildings and also the garden and croft or onset thereto adjoining and belonging containing two acres and all that paper mill with dwelling house drying houses and all other outbuildings thereto adjoining and belonging and commonly called Springside with Pingle thereto also adjoining containing ½ acres and all that fulling mill late in the tenure of Jonathan Willson and also three closes*' - Catskin or Coltskin Close, Barnapit Close and Little Bardill containing four acres in all and 30 acres of land in the open fields. The messuage was referred to as 'Freeman's', but is now known as Tealby Vale in Caistor Lane (Figs 21 & 22). In order to finance the purchase, Michael Gresham and others took a mortgage of £1,500 from John Willson at 4% interest. The other mortgagees were Thomas Gresham, yeoman of Tealby and Robert Webster, butcher of Tealby. If they severally failed to repay the loan the penal sum was £3,000. Thomas was probably Michael's twenty-one-year-old son. When Thomas Freeman had purchased Springside mill in 1772

for £430, he took out a mortgage for £300 with Richard Read. This mortgage was transferred to Michael Gresham in December 1792.

At the time of the enclosure of 1792 to 1795, Michael Gresham was obviously very active in exchanging various plots of land with other landowners. On completion of the enclosure he owned:-

Lower Papermill and Slip (Field 20)	0a 3r 4p
Homestead (30)	2a 0r 0p
Lane and site of mill, a road (45)	0a 1r 6p
Little Bardale (255)	0a 2r 25p
Part of Great Dales (46) (from Martinson)	1a 2r 36p
Part of Dale Mires (47) (from Manners)	0a 2r 26p
Long Catskin Close (19) (from Stourton)	1a 2r 26p
Allotted in Low North Field	19a 3r 8p

The allotted arable land was in lieu of land of equal value in the open fields.

Michael Gresham's watermark on his paper was M GRESHAM with the year date (Fig. 23). It can be seen on the paper used for writing the Land Tax returns for Binbrook, Kirkby, Thorganby and Walesby in 1797[18]. In the same year he was the tax collector in Tealby and he signed his name Michael Grasham, whereas the list of taxpayers shows him as Gresham.

On 11 April 1794 Michael Gresham insured the utensils and stock in trade at both the High and Lower Papermills[19] for a total of £1,550. On 27 November 1797 there was a John Grassham, farmer, buried in Tealby. It is not known what relationship he was to Michael; he may have been his brother who was born in 1746.

Fig. 23: Michael Gresham's watermark dated 1794. (courtesy Lincolnshire Archives Office and Mark Deyncourt)

Fig. 24: The signature of Michael Gresham (courtesy Lincolnshire Archives Office and Mark Deyncourt)

Michael Gresham was declared a bankrupt at a commission in Westminster on 7 December 1798 and the *London Gazette* reported on 1 to 5 January 1799 that:

'Whereas a Commission of Bankrupt is awarded and issued forth against Michael Grassham, late of Tealby, in the county of Lincoln, paper maker, dealer and chapman [travelling trader]*, and he being declared a bankrupt, is hereby required to surrender himself to the commissioners in the said commission named or the major part of them on the 10th and 11th days of January instant, and on the 12th day of February next, at ten o'clock in the forenoon on each of the said days, at the Bull Inn in Horncastle ... All persons indebted to the said Bankrupt or that have any of his effects are not to pay or deliver the same but to whom the commissioners shall appoint, but give notice to Mr. Clitherow, Attorney in Horncastle aforesaid. ...[The] commission found that the said Michael Gresham did for four years and upwards last past before the date and suing forth of the said commission carry on the trade and business of a paper maker and during all such time did seek and endeavour to get his living by buying large quantities of rags old ropes and other materials and manufacturing the same into paper and selling the same when so manufactured and became indebted to Henry Martinson in the sum of £409 upwards'.*

This sum was equivalent to the total value of one of the paper mills. Since Michael Gresham was using old ropes and other materials, he was probably making coarser papers, usually dyed, for wrapping as well as quality writing paper with watermarks.

On 28 January 1799 Richard Clitherow, solicitor in Horncastle, issued the following notice on behalf of the assignees of Michael Gresham's estate-

'Lincolnshire- Grasshams (sic) *Bankruptcy...Whereas the assignees under this commission have great reason to believe that large quantities of the bankrupts furniture, plate, linen, paper and other effects have been fraudulently secreted and conveyed away, since he became a bankrupt. -Notice is therefore given that a reward of £10 per Centrum will be allowed to any person or persons who will discover the party or parties who took the same away, or who are now in possession of any part thereof, as that the same may benefit the creditors. And any person in whose hands the same have been deposited who will deliver the same to the assignees, shall be allowed the same reward, and no further questions asked'.*

It must be assumed that the assignees thought that Michael Gresham himself had taken the property.

An advertisement appeared in the *Lincoln, Rutland and Stamford Mercury* on 15 March 1799: -

'To be sold by auction at the Bull Hotel, in Horncastle, on 23 March. Two capital paper mills, late the estate of Michael Gresham, a bankrupt.
Lot 1. All that capital freehold paper mill, standing at Tealby, with vats, presses etc., now in full employ.
Lot 2. The term of 7 years to come of the lease for 15 years in one other capital paper mill upon the same stream'.

Christopher Dinsdale of Tealby purchased the freehold mill (Springside) for £630 and the lease on High Paper Mill was taken over by John Clarke for £15 a year. This rent was only a quarter of the amount that Michael Gresham had been paying. On another occasion, Charles Milson, a grazier from Legsby, purchased the homestead and most of the farmland for £867 16s 3d. Edward Whitehead who was born in Tealby, but who at the time was a papermaker in Leasingham, purchased the mill site (formerly a fulling mill) and two acres. The mortgage taken out with John Willson was assigned to Richard Clitherow on 27 December 1799. The outstanding amount was £1,625, which implies that no interest had been paid during the

Fig. 25: The signature of Joshua Gibbons (courtesy Lincolnshire Archives Office and Mark Deyncourt)

previous two years.

Michael and Elizabeth Gresham left Tealby and went to live at Leasingham, near Sleaford. At that time Edward Whitehead, who was born in Tealby, was a papermaker in partnership with Samuel Cropper at Leasingham. Michael's son, Thomas, married Mary Mager at Yarburgh near Louth on 6 July 1797 and they had nine children, John, Michael Mager (baptised at Yarburgh in 1799), Mary Ann (baptised at Leasingham 1800); Elizabeth (baptised at Yarburgh in 1803) and four baptised in Tealby - Sarah (1806); Harriet (1814); James (1817), Jesse (1818) and George. So Thomas obviously went to Leasingham to join his parents but then returned to Tealby sometime between 1803 and 1806. Thomas was described as a papermaker on the baptism records in Tealby. Michael Mager married Caroline Shilling in Sculcoates, Hull on 22 December 1823; he died in Hull on 24 October 1864 and his death certificate described him as a papermaker. Mary Ann married James Cottam at Kingerby on 21 January 1822 and went to live in America. Elizabeth married William Patchett and emigrated to America and Sarah married William Clarke at Yarburgh in 1835 and lived at Grimoldby. Jesse died at age of three days. George also emigrated to America. When Thomas died on 26 February 1865 he was a farmer in Yarburgh. He left £20 to each of his children and all the farming stock to his son John. The total value of his proven will was less than £450.

Not much is known about the later years of Michael Gresham's life but it seems that he had been an entrepreneur and tried to expand too quickly and over extended himself or else the economics of papermaking were not very good at the time he began the business. The *Lincoln, Rutland and Stamford Mercury* reported on 17 February 1815 as follows: *'Died at Louth on 3rd inst. Aged 77, Mr. Gresham formerly of Tealby'*. At that time Michael Gresham would have been 75. The burial records for St James, Louth show that Mary Gressam

(widow) from Louth, aged 77 was buried on 5 February 1815. There are several possible explanations for these conflicting pieces of information. The newspaper report may have typed Mr instead of Mrs. It seems odd that both reports were more or less simultaneous and both had the age of 77. If it was Michael Gresham, he or the newspaper reported his age incorrectly and that he was buried elsewhere. If it was Mary Gressam, it is not apparent who she was.

Fig. 26: Joshua Gibbons's gravestone in Tealby churchyard

Joshua Gibbons (1778-1871)

Joshua Gibbons was the son of Edward (d. 1793) and Ann Gibbons (1743-1819) and was baptised in Tealby on 7 November 1778. Joshua's mother was born in Tealby and was the daughter of Joshua Clifton and his parents were married at Tealby on 14 May 1767. The Land Tax listing for 1791 shows Edward Gibbons as a tenant of John Clifton and paying 8/- tax. In 1814 Joshua bought the cottage that his widowed mother was living in for £31 10s. Joshua's mother had been paying a peppercorn rent to John Clifton, a farmer from Legsby; he was probably a relation because her maiden name was also Clifton. Charles Wigelsworth, the twenty-year-old son of Charles Wigelsworth who was the partner of John Clarke, paper manufacturer in Louth, drew up the agreement. The third party to the agreement was John Dinsdale, papermaker and son of Christopher Dinsdale the papermaker. The Poll Books of 1832, 1835 and 1841 describe Joshua as a freeholder and papermaker. It is highly likely that he worked at the Dinsdale paper mill. When he was 74 years old the 1852 Poll Book describes him as a freeholder but no longer as a papermaker. Joshua was a fiddler and between 1823 and 1826 he collected together 186 tunes and wrote them down in a notebook of handmade paper made in 1818 by Daniel Newman of Hollingbourne, Kent. Many of the tunes are in the keys of C and F, some were harmonised for two or three instruments and some were religious or marching music. Militia or volunteer bands would have played the marches in the post-Napoleonic time. At some stage he married Elizabeth Page who was born in 1778 in Faldingworth. Joshua was the enumerator for the 1841 census and Joshua and Elizabeth were living in a cottage in Bayons Park. In 1851, their niece, Hannah Page (born 1809 in Spridlington), was staying with them. Elizabeth died on 21 March 1859 aged 81 and in 1861 Hannah was housekeeper for Joshua. Joshua sold his cottage to his niece for £150 in 1869 and he died on 25 October 1871, aged 92. Joshua and Elizabeth are buried next to each other on the north side of Tealby churchyard and their niece is in the adjacent grave (Fig. 26).

Edward Whitehead (1756-1846)

Edward Whitehead was the son of Edward (1731-1818) and Elizabeth (1730-1814) Whitehead and was baptised in Tealby on 9 April 1756. In 1770 Edward (senior) was a papermaker in Tealby. Elizabeth was a member of the Methodists in Tealby in 1784 and 1785 and she was

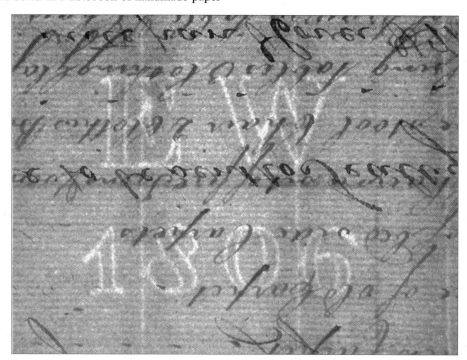

Fig. 27: Edward Whitehead's watermark showing 'EW 1806' (courtesy Lincolnshire Archives Office and Mark Deyncourt)

described as a spinner. Edward also had a sister, Elizabeth (1758-1769). Edward married Eleanor (Hellen or Ellen) Harrison in Tealby on 1 May 1780; she was the daughter of John (1734-1813) and Mary (1726-1794) Harrison of Tealby. Edward (junior) was in partnership with Samuel Cropper, as papermakers in Leasingham in 1800. The following report appeared in the *London Gazette* on 3 and 7 June 1800 and the *Lincoln, Rutland and Stamford Mercury* on 13 June 1800 *'The partnership lately subsisting between Samuel Cropper of New Sleaford, and Edward Whitehead of Leasingham, County of Lincoln, papermakers, dissolved by mutual consent, May 17 1800. The business in future will be carried out by the said Samuel Cropper. All debts standing due to and owing from the said partnership will be paid and received by Edward Whitehead, aforesaid'*.

Edward Whitehead moved back to Tealby in 1800 when he was aged 44 and bought a mill site and two acres from Michael Gresham's creditors for £106. The mill site had been a fulling mill until about 1792. The 1800 Land Tax return shows him as owner/occupier and paying one shilling and three pence rent. Edward Whitehead built a

new paper mill on the site and took out a mortgage on 28 January 1801 for £400 from John Kneave, a grocer from Church Hill, Tealby. On 28 January 1803 the *Lincoln, Rutland and Stamford Mercury* reported *'On Monday night, between 9 and 10 o'clock, an alarming fire broke out in the new paper mill belonging to Mr E Whitehead of Tealby, in this county, which in a short time nearly destroyed the same.'* He rebuilt it again and repaid his mortgage in 1817. Edward made white writing paper and used the watermark 'E W' with the year date beneath and Britannia in an oval surround with a crown above. The example at figure 27 with the date 1806 can be seen in the Lincolnshire Archives[20].

Edward continued to make paper until 1826, when he was 70. He then let the mill to William Smith who became a bankrupt in 1829[21]. The 1826 edition of White's Directory described William Smith as a papermaker at Springside mill; this was probably an error. The mill was advertised to be let in the *Lincoln, Rutland and Stamford Mercury* on 31 March 1831 and Edward Whitehead took out an insurance policy[22] on 12 December 1831 on the dwelling house; it was described as *'Dwelling house brick*

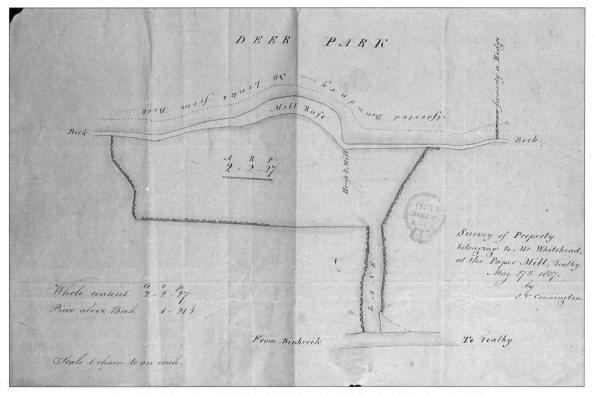

Fig. 28: Plan dated 27 May 1837 showing the land at Whitehead's Mill
(courtesy Lincolnshire Archives Office and Mark Deyncourt)

and stone and tiled £200'.

In 1837 there was a dispute between Edward Whitehead and his neighbour from Bayons Manor, Charles Tennyson d'Eyncourt, about the boundary between their respective properties. Edward claimed ownership of a 36-chain (about eight hundred yards) strip of land on the south side of the stream. Charles Tennyson d'Eyncourt's agent, William Cooper, had a survey conducted of Edward Whitehead's property (Fig. 28) and disputed the claim, saying that he had never heard of such a claim in Charles father's lifetime. In 1838 there was a draft agreement drawn up by Charles Tennyson d'Eyncourt to purchase the mill. A notice was printed in the *Lincoln, Rutland and Stamford Mercury* on 5 April 1839 to announce the sale by private contract to come into force in May. The notice described Edward as a papermaker and the proprietor. The property consisting of *'a freehold and commodious mill situate upon a powerful stream of water, and drying lofts, drying shades, store rooms, rag-house, stove room, barn stables and wagon-house, besides two cottages for the occupation of workmen. Adjoining the mill is a messuage in which the proprietor at present resides'.* Edward Whitehead eventually sold the mill with two acres to Charles Tennyson d'Eyncourt in 1845 for £325 and he also received an annuity of £7 a year for life. Edward's health was obviously failing because his first signature was very 'spidery' and he only put his mark on the receipt part of the agreement. The sale included some fixtures bought from the late tenant, Edward Smith, possibly the son of William Smith, who had become a bankrupt in 1829.

There is stone tablet on Watermill House, Sandy Lane inscribed 'EW 1790', and some people think this was Edward Whitehead, the papermaker, but it was in fact Edward Wheatcroft, a miller who became a bankrupt 1799.

Edward and Ellen Whitehead had three daughters, Sarah (1781), Elizabeth (1782) and Mary (1786). Elizabeth married Israel Brice (b. 1777) from Walesby on 23 August 1802. Elizabeth was buried at Tealby on 13 February 1826. Israel's father, Thomas Brice, was the tenant of High Papermill in 1816. Thomas died before 1825 because according to John Thorpe's valuation of Tealby (1825), his representatives were occupying the mill and 40 acres. Ellen was buried on 5 February 1838, aged 78. At the time of the 1841 census, Edward (85) was living in Prospect Street (i.e. Front Street) with his two surviving daughters, Sarah Hill (60) and Mary Whitehead (54). Edward was buried at Tealby on 9 April 1846, aged 90. Mary was still unmarried at the time of the 1861 census.

Christopher Dinsdale (1757-1835)

Christopher Dinsdale was the son of Thomas and Mary Dinsdale and was baptised in Tealby on 29 July 1757; Thomas was a tailor in Tealby. Christopher married Alice Stourton on 4 May 1787. She had been baptised in Tealby on 7 March 1754. She was a great-granddaughter of Thomas Stourton the Rector of Walesby and a second cousin once removed from Edward Stourton the younger, the papermaker in Tealby. They had five children, Mary (1788-1788), John (1789-1816), twins Mary (1790-1816) and Elizabeth (1790-?) and Robert (1793-1793). Alice died in 1814 aged 61 and then Christopher married Margaret the widow of William Brooks who had died in January 1813. Margaret died at Tealby on 17 August 1835 aged 72 and Christopher died eleven days later (aged 78). The parish register shows thirteen deaths from small pox between July and November 1836, so this may have been the cause of their deaths.

Between 1791 and 1799 Christopher Dinsdale was paying 4/- Land Tax as an owner-occupier. At the time of the Tealby enclosure award of 1792 to 1795 he owned a one-acre plot with a house on the corner of Caistor Lane

Fig. 29: The signature of Christopher Dinsdale (courtesy Lincolnshire Archives Office and Mark Deyncourt)

*Fig. 30: An example of Christopher Dinsdale's
watermark – C DINSDALE with 1802 beneath
(courtesy Lincolnshire Archives Office and Mark Deyncourt)*

and Papermill Lane, where the Old Vicarage is now situated
and a cottage on Rasen Road, opposite the top of Church
Lane. He was allotted the eight acre field where Wood
View and Willow Cottage are situated on Rasen Road.
In 1800 Christopher Dinsdale was described as a mercer
(dealer in textiles) and grocer when he purchased a paper
mill called Springside ('otherwise Lower Papermill')
and several small pieces of land from the administrators
of Michael Gresham's bankruptcy for £630. In 1802
Christopher Dinsdale took out fire insurance with Royal
Exchange '*on his water paper mill house containing one
stove but no steam engine, brick built and tiled situate at*

*Fig. 31: Christopher Dinsdale's gravestone in
Tealby churchyard*

*Tealby aforesaid £450. On fixed machinery and utensils
therein £250. On movable utensils and stock in trade
in the same £150.*' Christopher made writing paper and
he had his own watermarks. One watermark was 'C
DINSDALE' with the year date beneath. An example
for 1802 can be seen in the Tennyson Collection[23] at the
Lincolnshire Archives (Fig. 30). The other was just 'C
D'. His paper was used to write the details of the Land
Tax for Tealby. In some years he was the collector of the
land tax.

The Tealby Valuation in 1825 showed that Christopher
owned a '*house, buildings, garden and homestead*',
twelve acres of land and a '*paper mill, cottage and
slip*'. White's Directory for 1826 describes Christopher
Dinsdale as a papermaker and at that time Christopher's
stepson, William Brooks, was also a papermaker.
Christopher Dinsdale remained a papermaker until 1832
when he let the mill to Hercules Barnett. In 1832 the
property was subject of a mortgage of £1,000 to Thomas
Palgrave and Henry Woodhouse. In addition, Christopher
Dinsdale owed various other people £560. The property
was then conveyed to Messrs Bogg, Wright and Brooks
in consideration of the debts. They were some of the
creditors and acted as trustees. Hercules was born in
Nottingham in 1766 and married Elizabeth Shaw in 1819
at Hickling, (Nottingham). The Poll Book for 1832 shows
Hercules Barnett as a papermaker and Christopher as a
gentleman. Christopher Dinsdale's trustees subsequently
sold the mill to Hercules Barnett in 1834 for £500.
The Poll Book in 1835 showed Hercules Barnett as a
freeholder and papermaker from Hull. Barnett was living
in Winteringham in 1837 when he sold the mill to Charles
Tennyson d'Eyncourt.

Christopher Dinsdale wrote his last will on 14 April
1832 leaving '*all my messuages, cottages, mill closes
and land ... to my dear wife Margaret*' and his stepson,
William Brooks, was an executor. In 1833 he sold two
messuages, two cottages and 30 acres of land to Thomas
Palgrave and Henry Woodhouse, presumably to pay off
some of his debts to them. In 1834 he sold two cottages
and eight acres to John Bocock, yeoman of Irby, for £420.
The land was where Wood View and Willow Cottage now
stand. There were no cottages on the land when it was
allotted to him in 1792, so he obviously built them. Both
Christopher (aged 78) and Margaret (aged 72) died in
August the following year. When the will was proved in
January 1836 the value was less than £100. This small
amount is not surprising in view of the money owed

in 1832 and reflects the poor state of the papermaking industry at that time.

In an agreement between Joshua Gibbons and John Clifton dated 1814 there is mention of John Dinsdale, papermaker. John was Christopher's son and he died in 1816, aged 26. The graves of Christopher (Fig. 31), Alice and their children are at the top of the bank overlooking the Old Vicarage. Margaret's grave is alongside the grave of her first husband, William Brooks, beside the path leading to the south porch. It is probable that Charles Tennyson D'Eyncourt built the Vicarage shortly after the death of Christopher and Margaret Dinsdale.

Thomas Dent (1806-?)

Thomas was the son of Thomas and Elizabeth Dent and was baptised in Tealby on 23 March 1806. At the time of the 1851 census Thomas Dent (45) was described as a '*labourer, formerly papermaker*'. He was living in the area of Caistor Lane with his wife Maria (aged 41) who was born in Tealby and their four children. Between 1792 and 1820, there was a Thomas Dent occupying a property belonging to Thomas Freeman the papermaker until 1792. This was presumably the father of Thomas Dent junior. It must be assumed that both father and son worked in the paper mill.

John Petch (1769-1852)

Not much is known about John Petch and he did not know where he was born. He married Mary and they had at least five children, John (1799-1817); Jane (1805-1825); Robert (1809-?); Harriet (1811-?) and Edward (1816). In 1825 he occupied a house belonging to Christopher Dinsdale. At the 1841 census, John Petch (65) was living in Sand Hill. He was a gardener and Edward (25) who was a bricklayer and Harriet (27) were living with him. In the 1851 census John was living in the Caistor Lane area and was described as 82 years old, a pauper and a former papermaker. He presumably worked for Christopher Dinsdale. Jane's death was reported in the *Lincoln, Rutland and Stamford Mercury* on 18 February 1825. She was described as '*the daughter of Mr J Petch*'. Since his daughter's death was reported in the paper, John must have been of some importance. Harriet (39) was unmarried and living with her father in 1851; she was also described as a pauper. John was buried in Tealby on 17 October 1852 aged 83.

The Clarke Family

The Clarkes were a most remarkable papermaking family. The first known papermaker was Thomas Clarke who was born in Tealby in 1725. He married Ellen (Eleanor) Curtis in Tealby on 20 April 1747. Ellen was born in Buslingthorpe in 1727. Thomas had more than twenty descendants who were also papermakers. In 1751 Thomas's family were living in one end of a pair of '*cottages now much decayed.... near the fulling mill of Thomas Noel, now in the tenure of Nathaniel Bethel*' when it was leased by Edward Stourton the younger from Mary Camm a widow from Lincoln. Thomas was then aged 26, married with two children and was almost certainly working in the fulling mill. Thomas and Ellen had five children, Sarah (1748); Mark (1751); Mary (1754); Edward (1758) and John (1760). Thomas was a subscriber to build the 'Independent' house of worship according to the Dissenters Certificate for 1780. He signed his name 'with his mark' and both Thomas and 'Eleanor' were members of the Methodists in Tealby in 1784 and

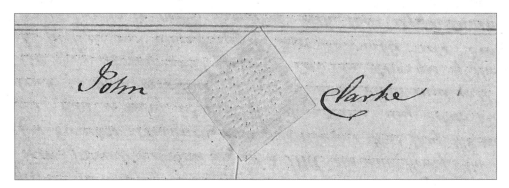

Fig. 32: The signature of John Clarke (courtesy Lincolnshire Archives Office and Mark Deyncourt)

1785. The listing shows Thomas as a papermaker and 'Eleanor' as a paperdresser. Two of their sons, Mark and John, also became papermakers. It is not known when Thomas first became a papermaker.

Mark (the eldest son of Thomas and Ellen) was described as a labourer when he married Faith Simpson at North Willingham in 1773. Mark later became a papermaker in Tealby, probably working for his younger brother John. Mark and Faith had five children (Sarah, Thomas, Christopher, Eleanor and Ann). Faith was buried at Tealby on 25 January 1819, aged 72 and Mark was buried at Tealby on 23 June 1828, aged 77. Their elder son Thomas married Mary Page in 1793; she may have been related to Elizabeth Page who married Joshua Gibbons. She died in 1799 and Thomas then married Mary Dracass in 1801. When he married in 1793 the witness was Michael Gresham and it is probable that Thomas was working for Michael until 1799 when he became bankrupt. When he married in 1801 he was described as a papermaker and probably worked for John Clarke (his uncle) until 1804 when John also became bankrupt. Thomas and Mary had five children: Sarah (1803); Eleanor (1805); Joseph (1807); Christopher (1809) and Paul (1811). The two oldest and two youngest were baptised in Tealby and Joseph was baptised in Louth. Thomas may have moved to Louth after Eleanor's birth to join his Uncle

John who had become bankrupt in 1804. Thomas returned to Tealby in 1808 or 1809 and then sometime after 1811 moved to Derbyshire with his family. This was possibly in 1812 when his Uncle John died. Sarah was a witness when her oldest brother Joseph married Mary Reader at Duffield (about six miles north of Derby) in 1823. Joseph served his time at Samuel Evans's paper mill at Darley, near Derby. Mary's family owned three paper mills on the River Exelbourne in Derbyshire. At the time of the 1841 census, Thomas was a papermaker at Samuel Evans's paper mill in St Alkmund parish (later known as Darley Abbey) in Derby. He died in 1847. His son Joseph owned the paper mill in Duffield prior to his own death in 1856. He died from drowning in the River Derwent after drinking at the Bridge Inn in Duffield. Seven of Joseph's eight sons were also papermakers at various mills throughout England. They were:- Adam (b. 1826); Thomas (b. 1830); Paul (b. 1833); Joseph (b. 1834); Andrew (b. 1836); John (b. 1839) and Silas (b. 1843).

The following is an extract from *The Paper-Maker and British Paper Trade Journal* dated 1 April 1908:

We have been favoured with a portrait [Fig. 33] of a group of seven members of the Clarke family, and we feel sure that some personal particulars concerning

Fig. 33: The Clarke family pictured in 'The Paper-Maker and British Paper Trade Journal' of April 1908

this remarkable group will be followed with the greatest interest.

Reading from left to right; the photograph presents to us John Clarke, Adam Clarke, Thomas Clarke, Paul Clarke Joseph Clarke, Andrew Clarke and Silas Clarke (who stands in the rear of the group). Dealing with the seven individually, we may state that:

John Clarke, aged 69 years is a paper-maker. Apprenticed to Tempest and Son, Little Eaton Mills, Derby. Worked for a number of years with Messrs. Cropper, Kendal, also worked some time at Phoenix Mill, Dartford. Now at Lower Tovil Mill, Maidstone.

Adam Clarke, aged 83 years, is a paper-maker. Served his time with his father, Joseph Clarke, who was proprietor of the paper mill at Duffield. He worked for some time at the following paper mills: King's Mills, Castle Donington; J. Baldwin & Son, King's Norton; and Tempest & Son, Little Eaton. He was also owner of the Duffield Mill after the death of his father. His eldest son, Samuel Reader Clarke, also a paper-maker has been with the firm of Smith, Stone & Knight, Ltd., Birmingham, for over thirty years, out of which he has been manager of their Union Paper Mill over twenty years. Samuel R. Clarke has also two sons working for Smith, Stone & Knight (one having been there twelve years). He was apprenticed at Little Eaton Mills, and previous to coming to Birmingham, was with Messrs. Cropper, Kendal. He was also for a short time manager at Tempest & Son's Little Eaton.

Thomas Clarke, aged 78 years. Worked for his father at Duffield Mill, as a boy. Was afterwards apprenticed as a carpenter and joiner with John Dawson, Duffield. Then worked for some time with Thompson & Fryer, builders, Derby, and also at Dover, but for most of his time he was with some of the leading firms in London.

Paul Clarke, aged 75 years. Served his apprenticeship with Tempest & Son, Little Eaton[24], afterwards at Helpstone[25], Lincolnshire, and Messrs. Cropper, Kendal. He was for the last fifty years with Tempest & Son, out of which he was manager for a considerable part of the time. He has a son now working at Brook Mills, Little Eaton.

Joseph Clarke, aged 73 years. Served his time with Tempest & Son, Little Eaton, where he lost four fingers from his right hand. He was for some time with Messrs. Cropper, Kendal; J. Baldwin & Son, King's Norton and Phoenix Mill, Dartford. He has been with Tempest and Son, Little Eaton, over thirty years. He

has four sons, all paper-makers: one at Springfields, Bolton: one at Smith, Stone & Knight's, Aston Mills, Birmingham: one at Brook Mills, Little Eaton, and the other at Hyde, Manchester. He also has a grandson working in East Lancashire.

Andrew Clarke, aged 72 years. Served his time with his father, at Duffield, afterwards at Helpstone, Lincoln, and for over thirty years with Tempest & Son, Little Eaton, Derby.

Silas Clarke, aged 65 years, was apprenticed at Little Eaton Mills, and is now working at Messrs. Cropper's. Kendal, where he has been for the last forty years. He has one son at Messrs. Cropper's and one son at Sandford, Oxfordshire.

Papermaking has been the trade of this interesting family for the last 200 years. The first one known to have been in the trade was Mark Clarke[26], the great-grandfather of these seven brothers. The writer has seen the indentures many times. He was apprenticed at Tealby, Lincolnshire. His son, Thomas Clark, was apprenticed at Samuel Evans's paper mills, Darley, near Derby. It was a 'five-vat' mill at the time, and he was the secretary, for the men working there, of the Old Society of Paper-makers. His son, Joseph Clarke also served his time at Samuel Evans's paper-mills and married a daughter of Mr. Samuel Reader, of Duffield, whose family were owners of three paper mills at different times on the River Exelbourne, Derbyshire. He was also an 'Old Society' man. Adam Clarke, the eldest of the group, who was the elder son of Joseph Clarke, took over the proprietorship of one of the mills at Duffield on the death of his father. At that time duty was paid on paper. He was a manufacturer of millboards for Bible covers, and also ledgers, pressing boards, and he easily held his own for that class of paper. The best boards were made from the old ropes[27] used on cages at collieries. Loading (or what is commonly called Derbyshire bagging) was unknown in that particular quality in those days. As soon as the tax was taken off paper[28], the English market was glutted with cheap German strawboards, in consequence of which, he was, with other small manufacturers, unable to continue at a profit. As will be seen, the Clarke family is well represented in the trade, by sons and grandsons of the seven brothers on the group, at the present time. Five of the group are 'Old Society' men. The five elder brothers are now retired and they are living in the village of Duffield[29], where they were born. They all enjoy good health and

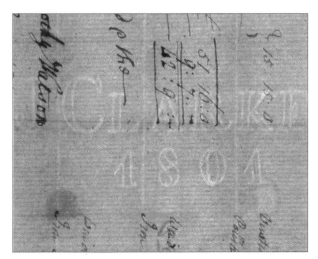

Fig. 34: John Clarke's watermark dated 1801. (courtesy Lincolnshire Archives Office and Mark Deyncourt)

have given the photographer an order to take them again when they are a hundred years.

Thomas and Ellen's daughter Mary married Mark Shepherd, a labourer, at Tealby on 4 November 1779. He later worked for his brother-in-law John at Louth. She was buried in Tealby in 1797, aged 43, and was described as '*of Louth*'.

Thomas and Ellen's youngest son, John (born 1760) married Mary Foston in Tealby on 17 April 1781. Mary (born 1756) was the younger daughter of John and Elizabeth Foston. Mary had an older brother John (born 1750) and an older sister Elizabeth (born 1755). John Foston died in 1786 and he left his wife Elizabeth '*that messuage or tennament situate in Tealby now in the occupation of John Clark*'. He also left her '*all my goods and chattles and movable affects together with an oak tree now growing upon or near the premises of the tennament aforesaid*'. John Foston also left another tenement (which was occupied by Matthew Smith) to his son John, five guineas to his daughter Elizabeth Harrison and two guineas to his daughter Mary Clarke. The will does not mention the house that John and Elizabeth were living in. They may have been living with the Clarke family because that is where his goods and chattels were located. At the time of the Tealby enclosure of 1792 to 1795 the Award shows John Foston and Elizabeth Howson (= Harrison) owning a homestead (plot 35). The plan shows two houses or buildings on the plot, which is where Valeside Cottage and Stockshill Cottage (16 and 18 Caistor Lane) are now situated. It is highly probable

that this is where John and Mary Clarke were living in 1788. The original houses were demolished and replaced by the present houses in about 1840. The plan also shows that John and Elizabeth Foston were allotted a two-acre field '*in the moor*' where Vine Cottage now stands on Rasen Road.

John and Mary Clarke had six children: - Sally (1782); John (1784); Christopher (1787); Christopher (1790) and Paul (1792) all baptised in Tealby and George, baptised at South Elkington, near Louth on 2 July 1798. Paul was buried in Tealby on 10 October 1795 and George was buried at Tealby as an '*infant from Louth*' on 21 July 1798. John's mother Ellen died at Tealby on 24 November 1791. John became a master papermaker, presumably learning the craft from his father, Thomas. John Clarke was in partnership with Charles Wigelsworth as paper manufacturers at Thorpe Hall Mill in Louth under the name of 'John Clarke and Company, Papermakers'. They had two watermarks 'CLARKE & Co', (this was used on paper to write the Land Tax for Tealby in 1796) and 'J CLARKE & Co' with a date mark (the Land Tax return for Binbrook in 1799 shows it with 1795). In May of 1795 '*a woman servant riding on top of a load of rags belonging to Messrs Clarke and Co of Louth was killed by the wagon being overturned upon her*'.

The partnership was mutually dissolved on 25 April 1798 and '*All debts owing from the said co-partnership shall be paid by the said Charles Wigelsworth; and that all sums owing to the said co-partnership shall also be received by him*'. Since all of John's five oldest children had been baptised in Tealby, it is probable that John did not go to Louth until about 1793. An advertisement in 1793 offered the following for sale:-

'To Stationers and Papermakers. A large substantial brick building well covered with slate, five stories high, 50' long and 20' wide within, well calculated for a paper mill, being situated on a stream equal to work four or perhaps six engines ... Canal within 1½ miles of the mill, a good turnpike road to it'.

On 2 April 1799, John was described as a paper manufacturer from Louth when he was assigned the remaining seven years of a fifteen-year lease on High Papermill for £15 a year (i.e. until 1806). Michael Gresham had held the first period of the lease (at £60 a year) from John and Matthew Stourton until his bankruptcy in December 1798. In 1799 John probably employed Thomas (74) his father, John (14) his son, Mark

(48) his brother and Thomas (23) his nephew.

John made white writing paper and used the watermark: - J CLARKE with the year date below. An example is shown here (Fig. 34) with the date 1801[30]

The following comment is written in the Parish Register: -'*30th January 1802, Robert Brown, aged 32, crushed to death in the High Papermill*' and this incident was reported in the *Lincoln Rutland and Stamford Mercury* on 5 February 1802 as follows: - '*On Friday last William (sic) Brown, journeyman to Mr. Clarke, papermaker, of Tealby, was caught by the wheel of the mill, and bruised in so shocking a manner as to cause his death in a few hours*'. A journeyman was a fully skilled tradesman who had served his apprenticeship.

According to a report made in 1939 by Edward Clarke, the great grandson of John Clarke, John sent a consignment of paper to America by a sailing vessel that was lost in the Atlantic, thereby suffering a loss of £1,000. A subsequent report in the *London Gazette* of 31 January to 4 February 1804 stated:-

> '*Whereas a Commission of Bankrupt is awarded and issued forth against John Clarke of Tealby, in the County of Lincoln, Papermaker, and he being declared bankrupt, is hereby required to surrender himself to the Commissioners in the said Commission named, or a major part of them, on the 29th Day of February instant, and on the 1st and 17th instant of March next, at Eleven in the forenoon on each Day, at the White Hart Inn, in Market Rasen, in the County of Lincoln*'.

The *Reading Mercury* reported John Clarke as a bankrupt on 13 February 1804.

It is not known what happened to John after his bankruptcy, he may have returned to work in Louth. John Clarke's father, Thomas, died five months later at Tealby on 6 June 1804 and was described as a '*papermaker and pauper*'; presumably he was a pauper due to his son's bankruptcy and his subsequent move away from Tealby. John's older brother Mark and Mark's son Thomas who were both papermakers may have managed the paper mill in Tealby and John's son Thomas (20) may have also helped. No records have been found that indicate any other tenants taking on the mill. John was buried in Louth on 23 March 1812 (the parish records show John Clark without the e). John's wife Mary then moved to Leasingham to live with her son John. She was buried on 2 April 1814 and was described as a 59 year old widow from Leasingham Papermill. Seven days later her ten year old grandson, Samuel Cropper, from Leasingham Papermill was buried; according to a newspaper report '*he was killed at Sleaford by the bursting of a cannon*' which may have occurred during the celebrations that followed Napoleon's abdication on 11 April 1814.

John and Mary's daughter Sally married James Cropper from Leasingham at Tealby on 23 December 1802. James was born at New Sleaford in 1781 and was the son of Samuel and Ann (nee Lomax) Cropper, who had seven other children; five daughters and two sons. Samuel was a miller and he was also a partner with Edward Whitehead in the paper mill on the River Slea in Leasingham parish, but the partnership was dissolved in 1800. Edward then moved back to Tealby where he was born, to buy a mill site (formerly a fulling mill) from the estate of Michael Gresham and to build a new paper mill. James Cropper owned the mill in Leasingham in 1802 and continued to make paper until 1807 when the mill was leased to the Rossington family. James and Sally (Sarah) Cropper had ten children between 1804 and 1823, all baptised at Leasingham. It was reported in the *Lincoln, Rutland and Stamford Mercury* on 15 November 1822 as follows:-

> '*Novel Circumstances- Baptised at Leasingham Church near Sleaford on Thursday inst., 21 children, all of whom, except one were from the paper mill, Leasingham Moor and seventeen of them of two families, viz.- nine of Mr. Croppers [eldest 16 years of age] and eight of Mr. Clarke [the eldest 15]*'.

When Samuel Cropper wrote his will in 1830, he was described as a miller at New Sleaford. He left his money to be divided equally between his daughters Catherine and Elizabeth and his son Samuel and he left James, his son, all the money that he had previously lent to him.

John and Mary's son John moved to Leasingham, probably to work at the paper mill for his brother-in-law (James Cropper), sometime after his father became bankrupt in 1804 and he married Elizabeth Wilson on 10 February 1807. Both were described as '*of this parish*'. Elizabeth was sixteen years old and was the granddaughter of Clement Rossington the papermaker from Leasingham. John and Elizabeth had eight children between 1807 and 1821, all baptised at Leasingham. They were:- Eliza (1807); George (1809); John (1811); Mary (1812); Charles (1815); Samuel (1817); Josiah (1819) and Edward (1821). John Clarke (junior) took the lease on the Leasingham paper mill in 1816 from James Cropper. In April of that year James Cropper was returning on the turnpike from Sleaford (now the A153) when, at about half past nine at night, he was robbed by three padmen (i.e. footpads or highwaymen on foot). They stole a five-guinea note, three one pound notes and about fifteen shillings in silver. About ten minutes later his brother-in-law, John Clarke was also robbed by the same men and lost his silver watch valued at £7 inscribed with the name 'John Clarke, Louth' (John Clarke of Louth, was his father). He also lost a pair of new shoes and a bridle.

Elizabeth Clarke died at Leasingham in 1827 when her four youngest children were less than twelve years old. In 1829 the lease on the mill was advertised: - '*The Leasingham Papermills, within two miles of Sleaford, and late in the occupation of Messrs. Stanage and Clark. Apply to Mr. J Mowbray, the proprietor*'. Mr Mowbray was a corn miller. In August 1829 John Clarke was described as a papermaker from Tealby when he signed a seven year apprenticeship for his fourteen year old son Charles, with Daniel Parker, a millwright in Tealby, so it seems that John moved back to Tealby in 1829 with his children after his wife died. In the 1841 census for Tealby, John's son Josiah (aged 22) was living in North Road and working as a wheelwright with Asaph and Mary Hill. Mary was Josiah's older sister. Asaph was killed in 1842 when a horse drawn cart that he was testing turned over. He left a wife and two small children, Asaph (4) and John (2). Mary then married Samuel Humphrey who was a beer seller at the Crown Inn, and they had three more children. Josiah's younger brother Edward (20) was in Queen Street and was an apprentice blacksmith with Matthew Gall. Charles went to Horncastle and set up as a millwright. His trade card was once nailed up in the five-sailed windmill in Spilsby Road, Horncastle and it read '*C F Clark, 3 Prospect Street, Horncastle, Millwright, oil, gas and steam engineer, brass-founder, 20 years experience in wind, water and steam milling. A trial solicited.*' His second son John, aged 21, was a millwright at Horncastle, and '*lost his life on January 14th 1861 on the Manchester, Sheffield and Lincolnshire Railway at Greetwell near Lincoln when a tyre on one of the engine wheels broke.*' He was buried at Horncastle six days later. It is interesting to note that this branch of the family dropped the 'e' from the end of their name. Charles's business must have run into financial difficulties because there is a report of him being discharged from bankruptcy in 1862. Josiah stayed in Tealby until he died in 1900. Edward went to Lincoln and founded Clarke's

Crank and Forge Ltd, which continued to trade until December 2002.

Thomas Brice (1772-1825?)

Thomas Brice was the second son of Thomas and Elizabeth Brice and he was baptised in Tealby on 27 October 1772. Thomas was a farmer from Risby and was the tenant of High Papermill in 1816. There was a Thomas Brice who was allocated 30 acres of land in the Tealby enclosure of 1792 to 1795, but it is not apparent whether this was the father or the son. Thomas died before 1825 because according to John Thorpe's Valuation of Tealby his representatives were occupying the mill and 40 acres in 1825. Thomas was married to Elizabeth and they had eight children: - Israel (1805-1854); John (1807); Thomas (1809); Hannah (1815); George (1817); Eliza (1819); Mary (1822) and Rachel (1823).

Thomas had two brothers, Israel (b.1777) and Charles (b.1782). Israel married Elizabeth Whitehead at Tealby on 23 August 1802. She was the daughter of Edward Whitehead who owned one of the paper mills in Tealby and she died at Tealby on 13 February 1826.

Benjamin Clark (1803-1827)

Benjamin Barkworth Clark(e) was the son of Joseph and Ellenor Clark(e) and was baptised on 21 November 1803 at Ashby cum Fenby, about ten miles north east of Tealby. According to the Excise List, Benjamin Clark (aged 22) was a papermaker at High Papermill in 1825. At that time he may have been a papermaker for the administrators of the estate of Thomas Brice or his father may have taken over the tenancy. The White's Directory for 1826 also describes him as a papermaker. George Tennyson's Rental Book for 1826 shows John Haddack and Isaac Robinson as tenants of High Papermill together with 75 acres. White's Directory may have been out of date or Benjamin Clark may have been their papermaker. According to the newspaper, Benjamin died '*very suddenly, in the prime of life*' on 2 July 1827 and he was buried at Broughton near Brigg three days later, aged just 23. A month later '*A valuation of several articles of property of Mr. Jos. Clark upon the premises of the High Mill amounts to £118-10s-0d*' was signed by Christopher Dinsdale and Edward Whitehead, the two other papermakers in Tealby. Mr Haddack paid '*14lb* (sic) *a part of rent for mill*' to Joseph Clark and Messrs Haddack and Robinson paid Joseph

Clark of Castlethorpe (a hamlet in Broughton, near Brigg) £100 *'for crop of corn'* on 12 February 1828. At the time of the 1841 census, Joseph Clark (65) was a farmer in Castlethorpe and his wife, Ellenor, was aged 60.

John Haddack and Isaac Robinson

George Tennyson's Rental Book for 1826 shows John Haddack and Isaac Robinson as tenants of High Papermill together with 75 acres. Strangely, four character references were made to William Cooper (George Tennyson's agent) in July 1827. The first was: *'We the undersigned residents of Grantham beg to recommend John Haddack and Isaac Robinson as steady, industrious, endeavouring men and if admitted tenants to the Paper Mill as they wish to be doubt not that they will do their utmost to fulfill all their engagements. John Brooks and Godfrey Gray'.* The second was *'Isaac Robinson, paper and rag dealer has kept a banking account at our bank for several years in perfectly satisfactory manner. Grantham Bank 1827'.* The third was *'This is to certify that I believe Mr John Haddack the bearer of this to be a steady and industrious man'.* The fourth reference stated, *'Sir, Isaac Robinson is my tenant and live under me 4 years and as always paid me punctual. George Hill'.* However, the *Lincoln, Rutland and Stamford Mercury* reported on 26 December 1828 that:-

> *'JOHN HADDACK   John Haddack, of the firm of Haddack and Robinson, paper manufacturers, Tealby, Lincolnshire, being in London on the 13th instant, called at the counting house of Messrs. Browne and Pretty, Chamberlains Wharf and obtained a written authority for his firm to draw upon them for £100 and £77 and has not been heard of since. All persons are cautioned against paying money or giving the said John Haddack credit on the partnership account; and if he is dead, any person giving information thereof to Mr. Isaac Robinson, Tealby, near Market Rasen will be rewarded for his trouble'.*

On 9 February 1829 William Cooper reported that *'I have had an interview with Messrs. Haddack and Robinson, the result of which is they are to leave at Lady Day [25 March], if they cannot sooner dispose of their property in the concern ... the rent paid by the present tenants is £150 15s 0d plus a cottage and garden at £4 4s 0d'.* On 20 February 1829 the mill was advertised in the *Lincoln, Rutland and Stamford Mercury* for letting with immediate effect: - *'An old established single vatted*

paper mill and the requisite drying houses, together with 23A 1R 38P of meadow and pasture land and 51A 2R 7P of arable land of superior quality with a farm house, engineer's house, barn, stable and other out buildings. The mill is adapted to the manufacture of paper of the best quality and possesses also a most desirable advantage in the first use of a very fine stream of spring water, with a spacious dam and good descents'. Applicants were requested to respond to William Cooper. On the same date the *Lincoln, Rutland and Stamford Mercury* reported *'Notice is hereby given that John Haddack and Isaac Robinson, of Tealby, in the county of Lincoln, paper-makers and co-partners, have by indenture 13 February 1829, transferred all their estate unto William Cooper of Tealby, yeoman and Daniel Parker, of the same place, millwright, in trust, for the benefit of creditors'.*

Hercules Barnett (1766-?)

Hercules Barnett was born in 1766 in Nottingham and he married Elizabeth Shaw in 1819 at Hickling, Nottingham. In 1832 he took the tenancy of Springside (Lower) Papermill from Christopher Dinsdale and he also agreed to purchase the mill for £500 and paid a deposit of £50. The Poll book for Tealby for 1832 shows Christopher as a 'gentleman' and Hercules as a papermaker. In 1833 Hercules insured the mill with County Fire Office[31] for £600 and he completed the purchase of the mill in 1834 and took out a mortgage with John Adams for £400. The Poll book for 1835 shows Hercules as a freeholder and papermaker from Hull. In 1837 Hercules was living in Winteringham when he sold the mill to Charles Tennyson d'Eyncourt for £488 (£400 was paid to John Adams to pay off the mortgage).

Jacob Watson

Jacob Watson, *'papermaker of this parish'*, married Hadakiah Jollands *'of this parish'* on 13 May 1796 at Tealby in the presence of Thomas Gresham and James Fenwick. Hadakiah's cousin, Agnes, was married to Francis Gunnell who was a papermaker in Barrow on Humber from about 1790 to 1800. At the time of the valuation in Tealby in 1825, Jacob was occupying a house owned by George Tennyson.

George Andrews (?-1797)

George Andrews, described as a papermaker, was buried at Tealby on 6 October 1797.

John Small

John was described as a papermaker in the list of members of the Methodists in Tealby in 1784 and 1785.

Mark Shepherd (1754-?)

Mark Shepherd was a labourer of Tealby when he married Mary Clarke the daughter of Thomas and Eleanor and older sister of John Clarke on 4 November 1779 at Tealby. Edward Whitehead, the papermaker, was a witness. Edward was then 23 years old and presumably had not at that time gone to be a papermaker in Leasingham. Mark and Mary had two children baptised in Tealby, John (1786) and Mark (1789). Their son Mark was buried in 1792 and Mary *'wife of Mark Shepherd of Louth'* was buried on 6 May 1797 aged 43 at Tealby. Mark *'papermaker of this parish'* then married Mary Beaumont in 1799. It is probable that Mark and Mary went to Louth to work with Mary's brother John. Mark presumably returned to Tealby to work for his former brother-in-law when he took the tenancy of Top Papermill in 1799.

Robert Brown (1769-1802)

The following comment was written in the Tealby Burial Register on 30 January 1802. *'Robert Brown, aged 32, crushed to death in the High Papermill'*. This incident was reported in the *Lincoln, Rutland and Stamford Mercury* on 5 February 1802 as follows: - *'On Friday last William* (sic) *Brown, journeyman to Mr. Clarke, papermaker, of Tealby, was caught by the wheel of the mill, and bruised in so shocking a manner as to cause his death in a few hours'*.

James Nutt (1734-1820)

James Nutt was born in 1734 and he became an apprentice to Thomas Harris (is this Thomas Harness?) in 1750[32] when he was sixteen years old. James, *'papermaker of this parish'*, married Martha Wright, *'of this parish'*, at Tealby on 13 July 1799 when he was 65 years old in the presence of Thomas Clarke. He was buried in Tealby on 25 April 1820, aged 86.

John Gunnell

John Gunnell, *'papermaker, of this parish'*, married Sarah Gladwin of Redbourn at Tealby on 18 October 1804. She was born in 1782 and was buried at Tealby on 13 August 1814. John's mother was Agnes (nee Jollands) and his father (Francis) was a papermaker in Barrow on Humber from about 1792 to 1800. He probably worked for Thomas Freeman who owned a mill in Tealby prior to 1792 and then leased a mill in Barrow on Humber. Agnes's father, Anthony Jollands, died in Barrow on Humber in March 1792 and he was described as a labouring man, probably working with Francis in the paper mill. Agnes's cousin, Hadakiah, married Jacob Watson, another papermaker. John and Sarah Gunnell had three children baptised in Tealby: - John (1807), John (1808) and Mary Ann (1810). Sarah died in 1814 and John married Ann White in 1830. At the time of the 1841 census he was a farmer living at Little Sixhills in Front Street and his father, Francis, was also living with him. John's brother, Christopher, married Sarah Wilson at Tealby in 1815. She was the daughter of Charles and Ann (nee Rossington) Wilson. Ann's father was Clement Rossington who was a papermaker at Leasingham and she died on 8 July 1826 at Tealby.

Samuel Leary

Samuel Leary was also a papermaker and he married Miss C Colebeck at Tealby on 15 January 1828. Miss Colebeck was the daughter of Mr Colebeck, a fisherman from Cleethorpes.

William Smith

William Smith leased Edward Whitehead's mill in 1826 (when Edward Whitehead was 70). William Smith became a bankrupt in 1829[33]. The 1826 edition of White's Directory described William Smith as a papermaker at Springside Mill; this was probably an error. Edward Whitehead eventually sold the mill with two acres to Charles Tennyson d'Eyncourt in 1845 for £325. The sale included some fixtures bought from the late tenant, Edward Smith, who was probably the son of William Smith.

Leasingham Moor Paper Mill

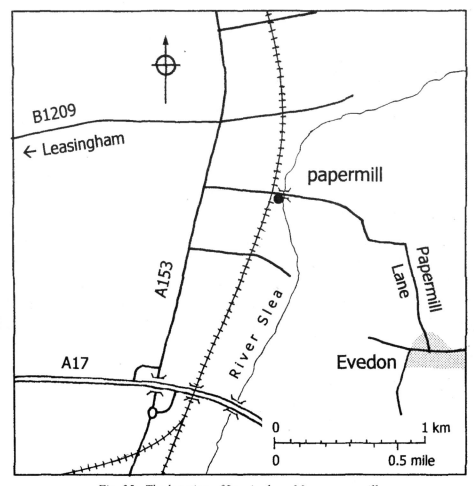

Fig. 35: The location of Leasingham Moor paper mill

Leasingham is a village about two miles north-north-west of Sleaford. There was a paper mill at Leasingham from about 1617. At that time the mill was known as Bardolf Mill and had been owned by Robert Brumitt, a corn miller who died in 1617. The mill (N.G.R. TF085485) was located at Leasingham Moor on the River Slea about one mile north west of the village of Evedon, which is three miles north east of Sleaford (Fig. 35). The site is beside a redundant lock next to Papermill Lane that connects the A153 road to the village of Evedon.

On 1 September 1612 'Danial' Turner married Anne Girland at Evedon and he was described as a paperman when their son Richard was buried at Evedon on 13 November 1617. Two months later Daniel's daughter Mary was baptised at Evedon. Nothing more is known

about papermaking at Leasingham until 1700 when Ann Turner married John Hollingsworth a papermaker at Leasingham. Ann had been born in Warsop but her father, Richard, moved to the Walk Mill at Leasingham, which was about ten minutes down the river from Bardolf Mill, with his family in about 1684. Richard had married Elizabeth Gilbie at Warsop, Nottinghamshire in 1675. Ann's brother-in-law Humphrey Fletcher wrote his last will when he was '*living now at the paper mill*' in 1718. The paper mill is mentioned in 1720 in Thomas Cox's *Magna Britannia; or Topographical, Historical, Ecclesiastical and Natural History of Lincolnshire*. Humphrey died in 1722 and his inventory included '*paper made....£35, rags....£5*'. The total value of his estate was appraised at £156. Humphrey had married Ann's sister, Ruth

Fig. 36: Painting of Leasingham Mill in the 1930s by Karl Woods. (from the windmill collection, Usher Gallery, courtesy of Lincolnshire County Council, reproduced by permission of the Benedictines of Pluscarden Abbey)

Whitehead (widow), at Evedon on 15 February 1707. Ann and Ruth's father, Richard, died in late February 1707 or 1708. Humphrey's son, Turner Fletcher, was described as a papermaker in Leasingham when he insured '*his stone and thatched house in Sleaford in several occupations*' in 1743[34] and he was still a papermaker in 1751 when he was shown as liable for Jury Service. Turner Fletcher married Mary Sharpe in 1753 and their daughter Mary married Clement Rossington, a master papermaker from Leasingham. Clement was mentioned in the will of John Bond in 1779. Two of Clement and Mary's granddaughters married papermakers; Elizabeth Wilson married John Clarke (son of John Clarke, papermaker from Tealby) and Sarah Wilson married Christopher Gunnell at Tealby. Clement wrote his last will on 14 February 1787; his trustees were his brother William, a papermaker living at Ewerby, and Turner Fletcher his brother-in-law, a grocer from New Sleaford. He left his estate to his daughter Ann and he died six days later. William died in 1793.

In 1791 or 1792 Richard Fletcher, one of the sons of Turner Fletcher, was shown as a tenant of the mill on the plans for the Sleaford Navigation Company. One of his employees, James Hackett (22), was found guilty of '*feloniously taking and carrying away from the house of Richard Fletcher of Leasingham, papermaker, divers goods the property of his master*' and was sentenced to be transported for seven years; the following year he was sent to New South Wales on board the 'Royal Admiral'.

John Clarke (senior) was born in Tealby. His father was also a papermaker. John went to Louth and was in business with Charles Wigelsworth but he returned to Tealby in 1799 and leased a paper mill until he became bankrupt in 1804. His daughter Sally married James Cropper from Leasingham, near Sleaford, at Tealby on 23 December 1802. James was born at New Sleaford in 1781 and was the son of Samuel and Ann (nee Lomax) Cropper. Samuel and Ann had seven other children, five daughters and two sons. Samuel was a miller and he was also a partner with Edward Whitehead of Tealby at the mill on the River Slea at Leasingham. The following report appeared in the *London Gazette* on 3 and 7 June 1800 and in the *Lincoln, Rutland and Stamford Mercury* on 13 June 1800:-

> *'The partnership lately subsisting between Samuel Cropper of New Sleaford, and Edward Whitehead of Leasingham, County of Lincoln, papermakers, dissolved by mutual consent, May 17ᵗʰ 1800. The business in future will be carried out by the said Samuel Cropper. All debts standing due to and owing from the said partnership will be paid and received by Edward Whitehead, aforesaid'.*

Edward Whitehead was born in Tealby two years after John Clarke. Edward Whitehead moved back to Tealby in 1800 to buy a mill site (formerly a fulling mill) from the estate of Michael Gresham and build a new paper mill. James Cropper owned the mill (then known as Cropper's Mill) at Leasingham in 1802 and continued to make paper until 1807 when the mill was leased to the Rossington family.

James and Sally (Sarah) had ten children, between 1804 and 1823, all baptised at Leasingham. It was reported in the *Lincoln, Rutland and Stamford Mercury* on 15 November 1822:-

> *'Novel Circumstances- Baptised at Leasingham Church near Sleaford on Thursday inst., 21 children, all of whom, except one were from the paper mill, Leasingham Moor and seventeen of them of two families, viz.- nine of Mr. Croppers [eldest 16 years of age] and eight of Mr. Clarke [the eldest 15]'.*

There was an advertisement in the paper in 1824 that read as follows. *'Wanted immediately, a steady youth as an apprentice to a paper-maker - for particulars apply to Mr. John Cropper, Leasingham Papermill, near Sleaford'.* John was the second son of James and Sally Cropper. He would have been aged nineteen in 1824.

John and Mary Clarke's son John married Elizabeth Wilson at Leasingham on 10 February 1807. They were both described as *'of this parish'*. Elizabeth was the granddaughter of Clement Rossington the papermaker from Leasingham. They had eight children between 1807 and 1821, all baptised at Leasingham. They were:- Eliza (1807); George (1809); John (1811); Mary (1812); Charles (1815); Samuel (1817); Josiah (1819) and Edward (1821). The excise lists show that James Cropper held the mill in 1816. John Clarke (junior) took the lease on the Leasingham paper mill in 1816 from James Cropper, who in April of that year was returning on the turnpike from Sleaford (now the A153) at about half-past-nine at night and was robbed by three padmen (i.e. footpads or highwaymen on foot). They stole a five guinea note, three one pound notes and about fifteen shillings in silver. About ten minutes later his brother in law, John Clarke was also robbed by the same men and lost his silver watch valued at £7 inscribed with the name 'John Clarke, Louth' (John Clarke of Louth, was his father). He also lost a pair of new shoes and a bridle.

It is not known where or when John Clarke senior died. Mary, his wife was buried at Leasingham on 2 April 1814. She was described as 59 years old and a widow from Leasingham paper mill and seven days later her ten year old grandson, Samuel Cropper, from Leasingham paper mill was buried; according to a newspaper report *'he was killed at Sleaford by the bursting of a cannon'*. This may have occurred during the celebrations that followed Napoleon's abdication on 11 April 1814. Elizabeth, the wife of John Clarke junior, died at Leasingham in 1827 when her four youngest children were less than twelve years old.

On 22nd June 1827 the following was advertised in the *Lincoln, Rutland and Stamford Mercury* for sale on 9 July:-

> *In Leasingham. A dwelling house and Paper-mill, sheds, and other offices and out houses, yards and gardens. A parcel of land (now planted with oziers) called Bank Piece, adjoining the Sleaford Navigation. And an allotment of newly inclosed land, on Leasingham Moor, adjoining the dwelling house and paper-mill. In the tenure of Mr. Samuel Cropper. 13A 2R 18P*
>
> *The paper-mill and manufactory possess a head of water of eight feet, a foreman's residence, workmen's cottages and every convenience for carrying on a lucrative and respectable trade.*
>
> *The corn-mill has a four feet fall of water, which drives two pairs of stones and there is a foreman's house and a cottage adjoining the mill.*
>
> *Both mills abut upon the Sleaford Navigation which empties itself into the river Witham where access is afforded through Boston to the sea: and through Lincoln to the River Trent, by which means a ready communication is opened with London and the western markets and with other parts of the Kingdom.*
>
> *The tenants will show the loss in their respective occupations, which possession may be had on the 6ᵗʰ of April next.*

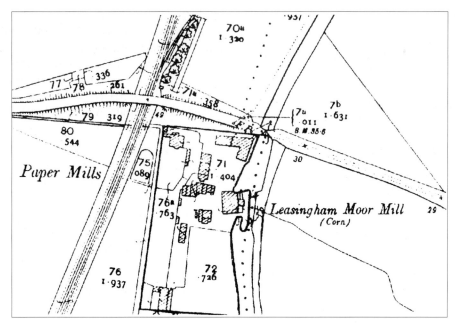

Fig. 37: Plan of Leasingham Moor mill and associated buildings in 1906 (Ordnance Survey, 1906)

Fig. 38: The site of Leasingham Mill in 2003

Fig. 39: The redundant lock beside the site of Leasingham Mill in 2003

Printed particulars may be had and further information obtained on application to Mr. Cragg, Threckingham, near Falkingham; or Messrs. Pearson, solicitors, Sleaford, at whose office a plan of the estates may be seen.

A notice appeared in the *Lincoln, Rutland and Stamford Mercury* on 6 July 1827 notifying the readers that the corn mill and Leasingham properties had been disposed of by private contract and the sale of the remainder of the estate had been postponed.

In the following year the paper mill was advertised again: - '*The old established paper mill and manufactory situate in Leasingham, in the occupation of Mr. Samuel Cropper, the owner.*' It seems as if Samuel Cropper, who was the tenant, purchased the mill in 1827. When Samuel Cropper wrote his will in 1830, he was described as a miller at New Sleaford and he left his money to be divided equally between his daughters Catherine and Elizabeth and his son Samuel. He left James all the money that he had previously lent to him. It seems that James was not a very successful businessman.

In 1829 the lease on the mill was advertised as follows: - '*The Leasingham Papermills, within two miles of Sleaford, and late in the occupation of Messrs. Stanage and Clark. Apply to Mr. J Mowbray, the proprietor*'. Mr. Mowbray was a corn miller. It seems likely that Stanage and Clarke had taken occupation in 1828. John Clarke was the brother-in-law of James Cropper. In August of 1829 John was described as a papermaker from Tealby when he signed a seven-year apprenticeship for his fourteen year old son Charles with Daniel Parker, a millwright in Tealby. So it seems that John moved from Leasingham back to Tealby in 1829 with his children. There are no records of papermaking at Leasingham after 1829. It is not known when John Clarke junior died.

The mill reverted to milling corn after 1829 and between the two World Wars it was the biggest mill on the River Slea (Figs 36 and 37). It had seven sets of stones and a massive waterwheel. Nothing now remains of the mill or the other buildings except the weir and a former lock; the buildings were demolished in the 1950s. (Figs 38 and 39)

Louth Paper Mill

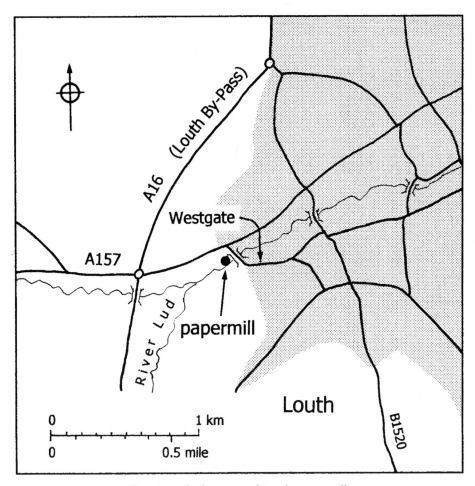

Fig. 40: The location of Louth paper mill

Thorpe Hall Mill, located on the River Lud at the west end of Westgate, Louth, (N.G.R. TF320871) (Fig. 40) was formerly a paper mill. The building still stands and in the recent past has been used as a trout farm but has now been converted into apartments. The original millpond and the weir with some remnants of the old mill wheel can still be seen at the back of the building. (Fig. 42)

A potential paper mill was advertised in 1793:-

'To Stationers and Papermakers. To be Sold. A large substantial brick building well covered with slate, five stories high, 50' long and 20' wide within, well calculated for a paper mill, being situated on a stream equal to work four or perhaps six engines ... canal within 1½ miles of the mill, a good turnpike road to it'.

Fig. 41: Louth paper mill in 2003

Fig. 42: The waterwheel arch and the remains of the waterwheel at Louth paper mill in 2003

Fig. 43: From an engraving in 'Sketches of Louth' by J W Wilson (1840). Note the louvred openings of the drying loft of the paper mill. (courtesy of David N Robinson)

Thorpe Hall Mill is about 1½ miles from the canal and was probably the mill that was referred to in the advertisement. Charles Wigelsworth a lawyer and banker bought the mill. He had been articled to Mr Bennett, an attorney in Barton-upon-Humber and when he was admitted as a solicitor in 1775 he took over a practice at 53 Westgate, Louth (Westgate House). In 1795 he was in partnership with John Clarke, trading as 'John Clarke and Company, Paper-makers'. They had a watermark 'CLARKE & Co'. Their paper was used to write the Land Tax for Tealby in 1796. John Clarke had been born in Tealby in 1760. Presumably, John provided the know-how and Charles provided the money. Charles Wigelsworth married Elizabeth Swift on 12 April 1791 and they had one son and three daughters. The partnership with John Clarke was dissolved on 25 April 1798 and was reported in the *London Gazette* on 1 May 1798. The same week the mill was advertised for sale, '*a new erected water-mill, for manufacturing the best writing paper with two vats, and all necessary out-buildings, for carrying on the said business. Also a good dwelling house with stables and garden and close ... Charles Wigelsworth, Attorney at Law*'. This all suggests that papermaking did not begin at

Louth until about 1794 or 1795. The mill was advertised for sale for a third time in 1800. There is a report of Edward Stourton of Louth, papermaker, insuring his paper mill in Tilby (Tealby) in 1755[10] (Fig. 5). The most likely explanation is that Edward had married Elizabeth Thorold from Louth in 1752 and his father-in-law had given him a half share in the lease of a corn mill in 1754. So Edward may well have just been living in Louth, but his paper mill was in Tealby.

Charles Wigelsworth had the first bank in Louth, at Westgate House. The bank entrance (now bricked up) was from Schoolhouse Lane. Charles was also the principal shareholder in the North Lincolnshire Bank, which was founded in 1790 and had its head office in Barton-upon-Humber. Charles's bank in Louth failed in 1799. This affected his mind and he 'died raving' on 27 May 1799 when he was only 54. The entry in the St James's Church burial register described him as a '*Gent. and friend to his neighbour*'. It is possible that the impending failure of the bank was the cause of the break-up of the partnership with John Clarke in the previous year. A notice in the *Lincoln, Rutland and Stamford Mercury* on 7 January

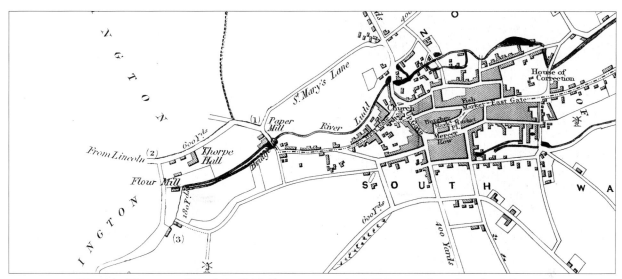

*Fig. 44: This map of Louth in 1837 (from a survey by R K Dawson based on the O.S. map)
shows the paper mill at the end of Westgate. (courtesy of David N Robinson)*

1803 reported '*Charles Wigelsworth, deceased, creditors may receive 5/- in the £ on 20/21 January at Kings Head Louth. To appear in person and on the following Monday at the office of Marris and Clarke at Barton on Humber*'. The North Lincolnshire Bank at Barton failed in 1812 leaving debts of over £200,000. The effect on the local economy of North Lincolnshire was dramatic, with over a thousand people becoming financially ruined. The paper mill was sold sometime after 1798 and Charles's widow, Elizabeth (nee Swift) continued to run the business with John Swift (possibly her brother) and trading as John Swift and Co. The mill was insured[35] in 1801 by Thomas James Birch Esq. of Hyde Park Barracks. The property was described as follows: - '*On a paper mill house with drying loft over brick built and tiled in South Elkington in the county of Lincoln, machinery and utensils therein £300. All in the tenure of Elizabeth Wigelsworth.*' Thomas James Birch was probably the grandson of James Birch and Margaret Bosvile. She was the daughter of the half-sister of John Bolle. These families had owned Thorpe Hall since 1602. It is not clear if the estate had formerly sold the mill and then repurchased in about 1798. The mill was again advertised for sale in 1809 '*To be sold. A very desirable water paper mill - held under lease to Old May Day 1811 at annual rent £100 then to 1818 at £20 per year when tenants interest expires.*' The excise list shows the mill as number 204 in 1816.

On 16 January 1818 an advertisement in the *Lincoln, Rutland and Stamford Mercury* mentioned '*a capital*

building now used as a paper mill with dwelling house adjoining, working houses, drying houses and lofts contiguous thereto, situate close to Louth ...now in the

*Fig. 45: An enlargement from an engraving by
Bartholomew Howlett showing the Louth
paper mill (1799) (courtesy of David N Robinson)*

Fig. 46: Postcard of 'The Old Mill, Louth' – the view from the back showing the mill leat
(courtesy of David N Robinson)

occupation of Mrs Wigelsworth...apply Messrs Paddison and Wigelsworth, Solicitors, Louth'. The Wigelsworth in the partnership was Charles (1794-1850), the son of Charles and Elizabeth. John Swift and Co also gave notice that they had taken another mill and that shop papers, writing papers, pasteboards, boxboards were being sold with rags to be taken in exchange. In the Louth valuation in 1823 there is no mention of the paper mill, however, John Swift was an owner/occupier in Westgate with a house, some warehouses and two paddocks, one called Papermill Close and Elizabeth Wigelsworth was also living in Westgate as an owner/occupier and Charles Wigelsworth in Walkergate (now Queen Street). The 1823 edition of Pigot's Directory lists Swift and Porter as paper manufacturers. In 1825 the partnership of John Swift, Elizabeth Wigelsworth and Michael Porter, trading as John Swift and Co was dissolved. In 1826 Elizabeth was in partnership with Michael Porter who lived at the mill. Elizabeth Wigelsworth and Michael Porter continued to make paper and John Swift carried on a paper business in a warehouse in Westgate selling machine and hand-made papers, boxboards and pasteboards and he offered best prices for ropes, rags, horsehair and quills. New methods of papermaking made it difficult to continue the business, and an advertisement appeared in the *Lincoln, Rutland and Stamford Mercury* on 20 January 1843 stating:-

'All that old water paper mill and premises on the river Ludd, constantly supplied with water and commodiously and well arranged for conducting business upon a very extensive scale. The premises comprise the mill, with a powerful water wheel and all other requisite machinery and utensils for the manufacture of paper, all in excellent repair, warehouses, drying sheds, stables and outhouses with a neat cottage residence, yard and garden. ... almost the only paper mill in the county, is calculated to ensure a trade of considerable magnitude to any active and responsible man of business'.

An advertisement to let the mill in April 1844 described the mill as '*has been producing coarse papers but recently restored to corn milling*' it had an eighteen foot waterwheel and three pairs of stones. The advertisement also included the following: '*Residue of the paper mill machinery consisting of three large screw presses, two large leaden pumps, a large double-armed boiler and a pair of hot pressing iron cylinders are to be sold*'. The mill continued as a corn mill until about 1920 and as late as 1938, the mill was still known as the 'Old Papermill'.

Houghton Paper Mill, Grantham

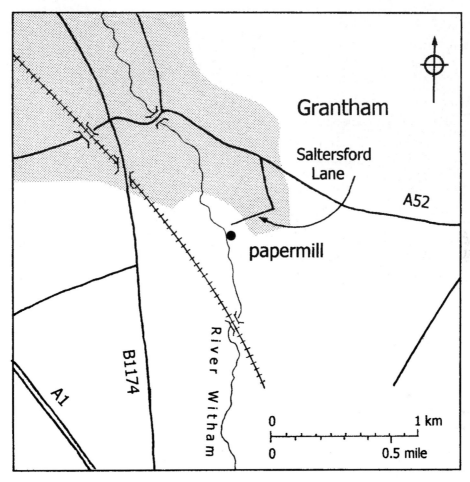

Fig. 47: The location of the Houghton paper mill at Grantham

Houghton was once a hamlet to the south east of Grantham but is now incorporated in the town. The mill (N.G.R. SK 925342), formerly known as Houghton mill, was situated on the east bank of the River Witham (Fig. 47). The site is just over a mile south-south-east of the main church of Grantham (St Wulfram's). There is still a road called Houghton Road on the west side of the river; it was previously known as Papermill Lane. The mill and lane are shown on the Greenwood 1827/8 map of Lincolnshire. There is a small bridge across the river just below the mill site and this is where Papermill Lane joined Saltersford Lane. There is a farm known as Papermill Farm on the location at the end of Saltersford Lane. The farmhouse, which has been extended at the southern end, divided into two and still has a Georgian doorway, may

well have been the mill owner's house (Fig. 48). All of the other original mill buildings have been destroyed but the mill foundations are still visible beside the weir (Fig. 49). The original course of the river has been diverted in order to achieve a sufficient height for the waterfall to power a waterwheel for the mill. Papermill Farm is now part of the Buckminster Estate, which is owned by the Tollemache family and the Harris family have been tenants since 1917.

The earliest known mention of papermaking at Houghton is in 1731 and 1735 when John Jessop was described as a paperman and papermaker in lists of persons liable for jury service in the County of Kesteven. James and Susannah Courtley, papermakers, raised a

Fig. 48: Papermill Farmhouse in 2003

Fig. 49: The weir at Papermill Farm (2003)

mortgage on the mill for £200 from Ann Still in 1742 and James Courtley, papermaker, insured[36] the mill on 27 April 1745:-

'On the stone and thatched house ... £50, on his household goods and stock in trade in the said house, £20 .... on a brick and stone part tiled part thatched millhouse with drying lofts over the same near adjoining the said house £200. On the mills utensils and stock in trade in the said millhouse and lofts £130. Total £400'.

A further mortgage was taken out in 1749 for £200 from Thomas Short, a butcher, Ann Short (nee Still) and Ruth Nash a widow from Grantham. Further mortgages were taken out with Ruth Nash in 1753 (£50), 1754 (£50) and 1759 (£100). James took Thomas Newland as an apprentice in 1762. Susannah (James's widow) took out a further mortgage in 1772. She sold the mill in 1774 to Philip Tallents, gentleman, of Newark-on-Trent and John Winter, yeoman, of Foston Turnpike in Great Gonerby, for £700. The proceeds were to be divided between John Winter and John Hoyes to whom she presumably owed money. Susannah also had to repay £580 still owing from the mortgage from the executors of Ruth Nash.

'The premises described as a paper-mill situate in Houghton, with a pingle about said mill of half a rood, a cottage house or tenement that stands upon the said pingle and a piece of ground called the cow-yard of one rood. The contents of the mill included machines, mortars, coggs, presses, vats, drying houses, utensils, working tools and implements used in or about or concerning the business of paper making'.

Messrs Winter and Hoyes raised a mortgage of £550 from Revd Robert Hall of Stubton. James Courtley, probably Susannah's son, a papermaker, took out an insurance policy[37] on 24 January 1775 *'On his household goods in his now dwelling only ... brick tiled and thatched ... £40, utensils and stock in trade therein only £40, wearing apparel therein only £150, utensils and stock in trade in his paper mill covered with tile and drying house adjoining ... £300'.* Presumably, James became tenant (possibly of Messrs Winter and Hoyes) after Susannah sold the mill. It is interesting to note the value of the clothes.

William Lupton of Ordsall near Retford and Thomas and Richard Lupton, both graziers of Aslackby (between Bourne and Sleaford), purchased the mill in 1787 for £850. There was a paper mill in Ordsall, which was where William Hemsworth, papermaker in Tealby, was born. William Lupton was born in Aslackby in 1753 and he married Elizabeth Nelson at Austerfield, Yorkshire in 1777. Elizabeth was the daughter of Richard and Martha Nelson of Barnby on the Moor and she had a brother called William who was a papermaker and farmer. William Lupton insured[38] the property at Houghton in 1787 and the policy stated: -'*William Lupton of Spittlegate near Grantham in the county of Lincoln gent. On his water paper mill situate as aforesaid **timber** £300. House near late in tenure of William Taylor, papermaker brick stone and tile £200.'* Spittlegate was a small village next to Houghton, but it is now a part of Grantham. William Lupton took John Humphry as an apprentice in 1792. In October 1793 the following advertisement appeared in the paper '*Wanted a partner in a three vat paper mill upon a ford stream well situated for markets and in full business, works entirely new. Apply Wm. Nelson, Barnby Moor or Wm. Lupton Houghton'.* An insurance policy[39] was taken out on 11 November 1793 by Nicholas Hutchinson of Southwell, surgeon and apothecary, who insured – '*a house, tenant William Lupton £150. On a paper mill occupied by the said William Lupton £450, both brick and tiled and situate at Houghton.'* It seems that sometime between 1787 and 1793 the mill was renovated from being timber to being constructed with brick and tile. In addition William Lupton had become tenant rather than being owner. Elizabeth Lupton's father, Richard Nelson, died at Barnby on the Moor in 1794 and in the same year the Nelson family built a paper mill on the west side of the River Idle at Retford. William Nelson's son, Horatio, described as a paper and pasteboard manufacturer, occupied the Retford Mill in 1830[40]. At the same time Richard Nelson was a paper manufacturer at Ordsall. A mill on the east side of the river in Albert Street, owned by Retford Wall Coverings Ltd, made ingrain wallpaper and continued to operate until it was partially destroyed by fire in 2002.

The partnership between William Lupton and William Dillon Smith trading as 'Lupton and Smith' at Houghton Mill was dissolved in 1794 and William Lupton took out insurance[41] in 1796 on the property viz.:- '*On paper mill with lofts and warehouse over situate at Houghton and having no communication with the dwelling house £300. On machinery £200.'* Another partnership between William Lupton and William Taylor, papermakers, was dissolved in 1798[42]. William advertised in 1798 as follows '*To Overseers of the Poor, wanted immediately, a strong healthy boy about 13 or 14 years of age, as an apprentice papermaker, for particulars apply Mr. William Lupton, Houghton nr. Grantham. NB a premium will be expected. Letters (post paid) duly answered*'. According to Excise Treasury letters William Lupton borrowed £500 on mortgage from Robert Turner a local druggist and in 1799 they became partners and Robert Turner advanced £600 as his share of the capital in the papermaking venture.   The partnership with Robert Turner was dissolved in 1800[43].   They had traded as 'Lupton and Turner'.   William Lupton then carried on the business and erected a mill to grind bones for manure in December 1800.   William advertised for two more apprentices in 1800 and again in 1806.

William's wife, Elizabeth, died in May 1807 and his only daughter married Samuel Foster, a corn factor, in January 1808. Two months later, William Lupton assigned over his personal estate and effects to Robert Turner, his partner and Gildon Manton of Spittlegate, a maltster and miller, in trust for his creditors.   His creditors were paid four shillings in the pound in June 1808 and another four shillings in the pound in October 1808.   William also transferred an apprenticeship indenture entered into in 1802 to Samuel Foster, his son-in-law.   In July 1809 William was an insolvent debtor and prisoner in Lincoln Castle for a debt of less than £200.   He was described as a papermaker formerly from Houghton but lately of Boston.   He was discharged under the Insolvency Act on 4 August 1809.

Robert Lupton, a gentleman from Bitchfield (seven miles south east of Grantham) sold the mill on 29 October 1809 for £1,750.   The relationship between Robert and William Lupton is not known, but they were probably brothers, since William had an older brother called Robert who was born in Aslackby in 1744.   The purchasers were

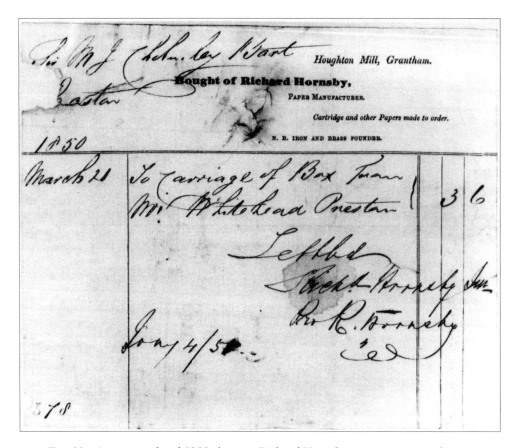

Fig. 50: An invoice dated 1850 showing Richard Hornsby as a paper manufacturer

William Nelson, a gentleman of Ordsall and Richard Foster, a miller of East Retford and Lucas Spillbury, a gentleman of Bawtry. William Nelson was William Lupton's brother-in-law. Richard Foster may have been a relative of William's son-in-law. The mill had been let to Richard Foster for £50 a year since 5 April 1808 on a seventeen-year lease. This ended the direct involvement of William Lupton after 21 years. He had obviously had many ups and downs over the years with several partners and finally bankruptcy and jail. According to various settlement certificates, William Lupton had employed the following people: - Samuel Reid (1787), Nathanial Wilson (1795), George Johnson (1800) and Henry Riley (1806). Settlement certificates were given to people leaving a parish and acknowledgment of the continuing responsibility of the parish of origin. If the new parish refused to give poor relief, the pauper may have been examined by magistrates and removed by force.

Samuel Foster and William Nelson continued in partnership until 10 October 1813 as papermakers and bone merchants under the name of Foster and Nelson. William Nelson died on 17 February 1824 and an advertisement for the sale of the mill on 15 October 1824 described the property as: - '*All that paper mill situated at Houghton, near Grantham in the county of Lincoln. Now in the occupation of Mr. Samuel Foster. The mill is worked by an excellent stream of water, situate a mile from Grantham, is well established, and has for many years been fully employed.*' The mill was sold by auction on 2 April 1825 to John Rogers, a baker, of Spittlegate and William Keeling, also a baker, of Little Gonerby for £1,780. They took out a mortgage for £2,000 from William Ostler a gentleman from Grantham. The agreement described the property as '*all that paper mill situate standing and being in Houghton and a pingle lying above the mill containing ½ rood and all that cottage house or tenement standing upon the pingle and a cow yard containing 1 rood.*' They continued trading as papermakers under the name of 'Rogers and Keeling' and the 1828/29 edition of Pigot's Directory listed them as paper manufacturers at Walkergate (Westgate). They got into financial difficulties and assigned their estate for the benefit of creditors in December 1832. Richard Hornsby, machine maker from Spittlegate, purchased the mill in January 1833 with the help of a £2,000 mortgage from John Minta, a farmer from Normanton. Richard Hornsby had been one of the founders of Ruston and Hornsby in 1815. An invoice dated 1850 describes Richard Hornsby

as a paper manufacturer (cartridge and other papers made to order) and an iron and brass founder (Fig. 50). A Parliamentary return in 1851 described Houghton Mill as having two beating engines in use. Richard continued the papermaking business until 1858. At that time he was 68 years old and was described as an agricultural implement manufacturer, papermaker and farmer. He then leased the property to Henry Bell, a corn factor from Grantham, and Henry Levick, a tanner from Little Gonerby. The annual rental was to be £1,000 until Richard's death and then £400 payable to his widow Mary Ann. The agreement specified that after Mary Ann's death, the property was to revert to their three sons, Richard, James and William. The site plan was included in the agreement and shows that the mill and ancillary buildings had a ground floor area of about 1,600 square feet (Fig. 51).

In 1862 Richard Hornsby and Sons were making '*grocery papers, browns, blues and purple papers*'. Presumably the tenancy had been terminated. Richard died in 1864 and Mary Ann died two years later. In 1871 a 48 inch paper machine was in operation, which was later replaced by a 54 inch machine.

In 1876 the Hornsby family sold the mill for £2,000 to Michael Jack, a papermaker from Peggy's Mill at Cramond near Edinburgh. The mill building comprised of a:-

'machine room - 49' x 18', boiler house and store room - 39' x 20', chopping room - 22½' x 22¾', grinders shop - 18' x 8', sole house - 41' x 20½', rag engine room - 27' x 22', sorting room - 35' x 22¾', cutting room - 27' x 22', sorting room - 35' x 22¾', cutting room - 27' x 14¾', 3 sorting rooms - 38' x 20¾', 20¾' x 18¼' and 18¼' x 18', stock room - 41' x 20½'. lumber room - 41' x 20½' carpenter's shop is attached to the mill and cottage and gardens.'

The agreement included the following details:-

'all that wrought iron breast water wheel and that wrought iron shaft, 16' in diameter, 12' wide and 11' fall of water now driving fourteen stones, rag engines and pump for supplying the same with water. And all that paper machine which is 48" wide with suitable machinery and apparatus affixed for manufacturing of brown and grocery papers'.

The total floor area was about 9,500 square feet. This is about six times the ground floor area in 1858 and presumably, the Hornsby family were responsible for the

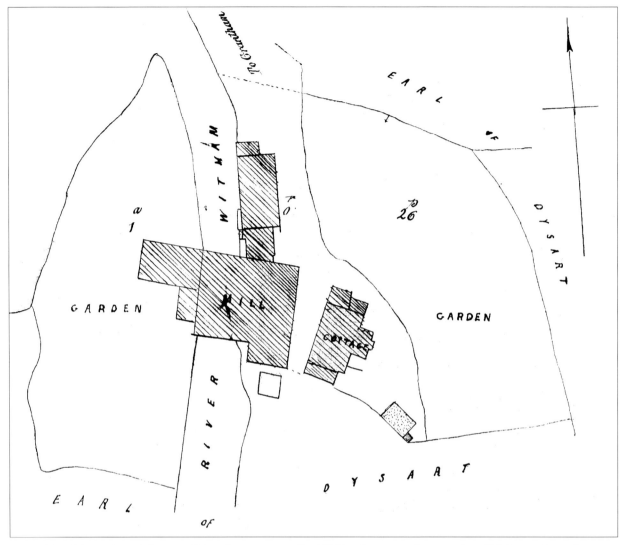

Fig. 51: A plan of the site of Houghton paper mill of 1858 - the original at a scale of 80 feet to the inch.
(courtesy of Sir Lyonel Tollemache)

expansion. The year after Michael Jack took over the river flooded and the dam on the west side of the mill was broken. Jack claimed that the Hornsby family was responsible for the repair costs because they were tenants on the grass banks of the dam. A court case resolved that Jack should install a floodgate and that the Hornsby family should pay £50 towards the costs and it was also agreed that Jack would repair any future damage at his expense. The following year the premises were assigned to the Nottingham Stock Bank when they lent Michael Jack £700. He became their tenant at a rental of £100 a year. Michael Jack borrowed £800 from James Hornsby in July 1880 and he repaid the Nottingham Bank. James

Hornsby lent a further £300 in September 1880. In 1887 one male and two female employees were still making paper. By 1888, Michael Jack owed James Hornsby a total of £1,233. The creditors agreed to transfer the mill to James Hornsby at a value of £900 and he was at liberty to pursue Jack's estate for the outstanding £333. Papermaking probably ceased at this time. Finally, James Hornsby sold the property in 1896 for £350 to the trustees of Rt Hon. Sir Lionel William John Manners (late Earl of Dysart). The Earl of Dysart owned the land surrounding the mill in 1858.

Barrow on Humber Paper Mill

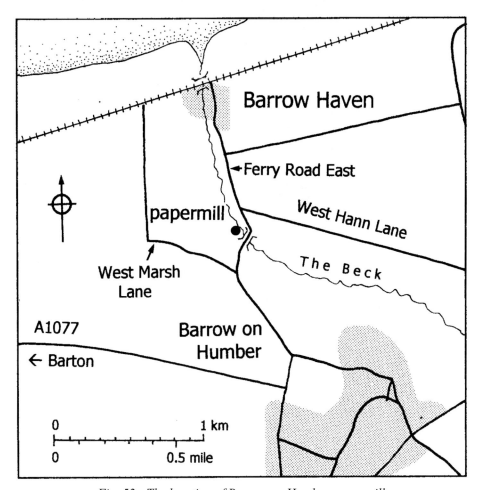

Fig. 52: The location of Barrow on Humber paper mill

Barrow on Humber is situated about two miles south of the River Humber between Barton-upon-Humber and New Holland (N.G.R. TA 063225). *The Town's Book of Barton* (1713) shows '*watermill is to pay to the Church every year 6s 6d*'. Richard Beck, a surgeon in Barton-upon-Humber owned a water mill in Barrow on Humber in 1728. In his will (1728) he left £2 10s a year from the rental from the mill for the education of six poor children. They were to be taught reading, writing and 'arithmatick'. A copper plate engraving by William Stukeley (1724) shows the mill on the west side of 'Beck Drain' just to the north of the bridge (Figs 53a and 53b). The engraving also shows Barrow Church and the earthworks of the castle. The mill was almost certainly a tidal mill. A house now called Watermill Cottage was built on the site in about

1995 and the stone foundations of the mill were located (Fig. 54).

In 1780, Thomas Houghton was described as a papermaker from Market Raisin (sic) when he insured his paper mill for £500[44] at Barrow on Humber which was in the tenure of Thomas Houghton (probably his son). The insurance also included a '*house only communicating £100, three tenements near £100 and a drying house near £200*'. All buildings were '*brick and tiled, total £900.*' Thomas Houghton the elder and younger, were both papermakers, dealers and chapmen (i.e. traders) when they were reported as bankrupt at Wilminton Mill, Sutton-in-Holderness, Yorkshire in 1788[45]. According to the administration of Thomas's estate[46], in 1827 he '*departed this life many years ago*', intestate. The value

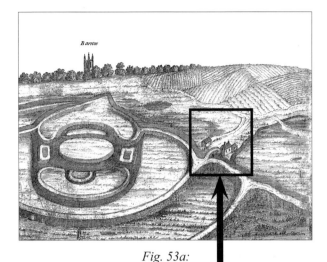

Fig. 53a:

of his estate was reported as less than £20. There is some confusion about which reports refer to the father or son. It seems likely that Thomas Houghton the elder stopped being a papermaker at Tealby in 1771, but his son continued at Barrow on Humber and at Sutton-in-Holderness between 1780 and 1788.

The enclosure award of 1803 shows Marmaduke Grayburn Esq. claiming:-

'Land, formerly Mary Longs, watermill and lands therewith formerly Becks [i.e. Richard Beck]*, devised by him to charitable uses. 70 acres open field, 9 acres meadow. Messuage in the occupation of Thomas Bell called Porch House also formerly Becks and devised as last mentioned. NB The last mentioned mill and messuage and land therewith are claimed by Thomas*

Figs 53a & 53b: A drawing dated 1724 entitled 'Prospect of the British Temple at Barrow, Lincoln' by William Stukeley, 'Antiquarian and Freemason'. The drawing shows the castle earthworks including the mill. A portion has been enlarged (in Fig. 53b) to show the bridge and other buildings associated with the mill (courtesy of Jon Sass)

Fig. 53b:

Freeman as lessee under Messrs. Grayburn' and 'in the ancient inclosures of the watermill scite and cottage and close lying opposite thereto within.'

The land was close to Barrow Haven and was bounded on the west by Ferry Road and on the north by Beck Drain. Thomas Freeman was originally a papermaker in Tamworth, Staffordshire, who leased and later purchased a paper mill from Thomas Houghton in Tealby in 1770. He sold that mill in 1792 and it is highly likely that Thomas Freeman and Francis Gunnell moved from Tealby to Barrow on Humber at that time. Francis Gunnell probably worked for Thomas Freeman in Barrow on Humber until about 1800. He married Agnes Jollands at Tealby in 1783 and their four eldest children were born in Tealby between 1784 and 1790. Their next two children were born in Barrow on Humber in 1792 and 1797; the second child (Sarah) died at Barrow on Humber in 1798 and their youngest child was born in Tealby in 1802.

The enclosure award of 1803 shows that William Grayburn Esq. was allocated '*all that other allotment or parcel of land containing five acres two roods and thirty six perches lying in the west marsh and bounded on or towards the east by an ancient inclosure of the watermill scite and the Ferry road.*' The plan shows the two buildings seen on the Stukeley engraving.

The 1890 Ordnance Survey map shows that the bridge is the '*highest point to which ordinary tide flows*'. At the time of the enclosure the bridge was called 'Watermill Clough'; the 'clough' being a sluice to stop tidal water from going upstream. The clough was situated '*near the late watermill*' in Watermill Field. There are remnants of the old sluice still on the bridge. A new sluice with higher riverbanks was built in about 1985 about 50 yards downstream from the bridge to try to prevent a repeat of the disastrous floods of 1953 when the area was covered with about four feet of water. This watermill site was almost certainly subject to flooding and was probably not viable in the long term. It seems to have ceased working in the late 1790s.

In 1793 to 1794 Thomas Houghton was living in a cottage in 'Butchery' next to Dovecot in Priestgate, Barton-upon-Humber. A Thomas Houghton married Ann Crowder at Barton-upon-Humber in 1794. He was probably the same Thomas Houghton who was the papermaker. They had three children baptised in South Ferriby; Mary (1798), Elizabeth (1803) and Thomas (1805). It seems that Thomas Houghton left Barrow sometime between 1780 and 1788 and went to Sutton-in-Holderness. He then returned to Barrow before moving to South Ferriby. It is not known what happened to the family after 1805.

Fig. 54: The site of Barrow on Humber paper mill is now occupied by a house named Watermill Cottage (2003)

West Deeping Paper Mill

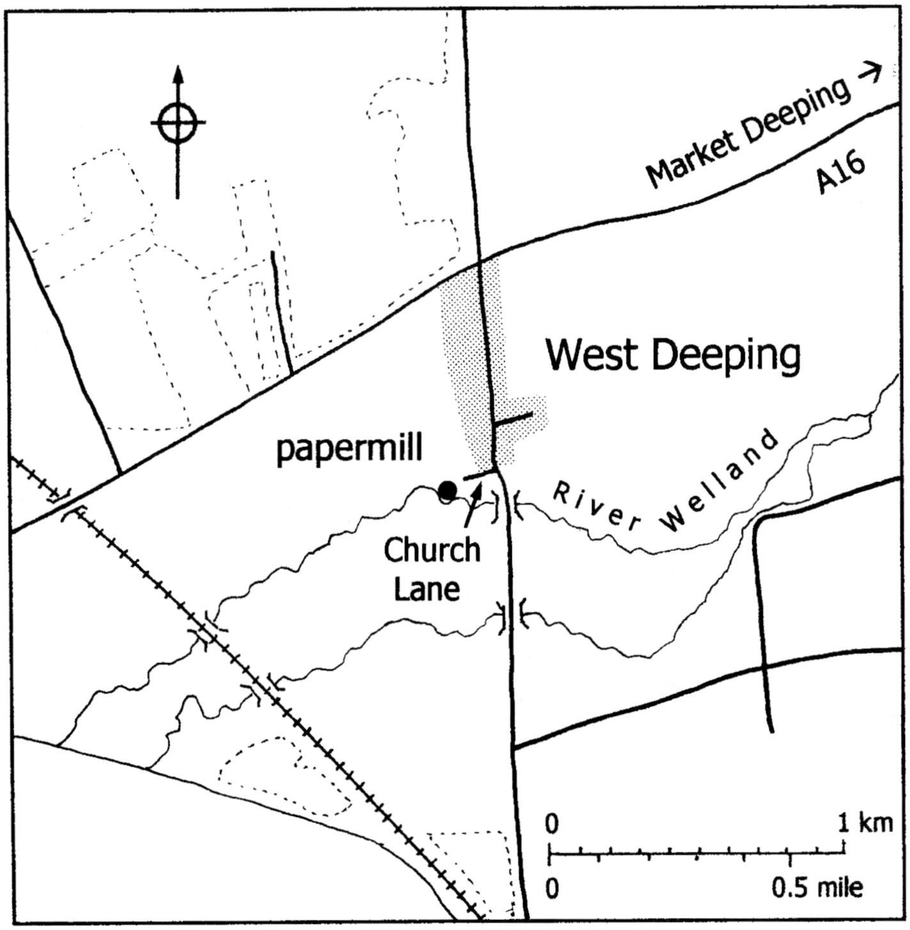

Fig. 55: The location of West Deeping paper mill

West Deeping is situated on the River Welland about five miles east of Stamford and one mile west of Market Deeping. Not much is known about West Deeping paper mill. The road through the village of West Deeping is a former Roman road called King Street. The mill was situated at the end of Church Lane and opposite the church (N.G.R. TF 108085) (Fig. 55).

Lewis Walker, a papermaker, took an apprentice named William Stanton in 1713. In 1733 and 1742 Thomas Goodhall, a master papermaker appeared on a list of people liable for jury service in the county of Kesteven. Richard 'Goodale' took out insurance in 1745[47] *'On his*

now dwellinghouse only ... stone and thatched £200, on his barn only in the yard stone and thatched £50, on his stable and offices adjoining the same and granary over them in the said yard stone and thatch £50, on his stock of raggs in his paper mill only £40, and on his implements in trade therein only £20...total £400'.

The mill was burnt down in the 1830s with the loss of two lives. It was rebuilt and used as a corn mill until the 1950s; it is now a private house called 'The Mill' (Fig. 56). Apart from the references above, nothing more is known about papermaking at West Deeping.

Fig. 56: 'The Mill' at West Deeping (2003)

Epilogue

Eight former paper mills have been identified in Lincolnshire; three in Tealby and one in each of Leasingham, Louth, West Deeping, Barrow on Humber and Houghton (Grantham).

The three mills in Tealby produced white writing paper with watermarks and may also have produced lower grades of paper. Two of the Tealby mills began production in the late 1600s or early 1700s. The third mill began in 1800. All three mills ceased production in the early 1830s.

Nearly forty individuals have been identified who were involved with papermaking in Lincolnshire in some way or another. Several of the principal families were related by marriage in the same way that fishermen, miners and farmers were, where the skills and craftsmanship were passed from one generation to another. There were several family connections between the paper mills at Tealby, Louth, Barrow on Humber and Leasingham. Many of the papermaking families were related; for example John Clarke (junior) (1784-1829+) was related to the following papermakers:

The papermaking industry in Tealby only lasted for about 150 years, but during that time there were four documented bankruptcies, one fire, two incidents involving theft and one accidental death. The families were also subjected to highway robbery and two other accidental deaths!

The paper industry in Lincolnshire ended due to a combination of increased competition from mechanical processes, excise taxes, the remoteness from customers, the high price and the difficulties of importing the raw materials.

> There is an old saying: 'rags make paper,
> paper makes money, money makes bank
> notes, bank notes makes loans, loans
> make beggars, beggars make rags'.

Thomas Clarke (1725-1804)	grandfather	Tealby
John Clarke (1760-1812)	father	Tealby, Louth, Leasingham
Mark Clarke (1751-1828)	uncle	Tealby
Thomas Clarke (1776-1847)	cousin	Tealby, Darley
Joseph Clarke (1806-1856)	first cousin once removed	Duffield
Five sons of Joseph Clarke	first cousins twice removed	various
Humphrey Fletcher (1672-1722)	wife's great great grandfather	Leasingham
Richard Fletcher (1767-?)	wife's great uncle	Leasingham
Clement Rossington (1747-1787)	wife's great grandfather	Leasingham
William Rossington (<1747-1793)	wife's great uncle	Leasingham
Mark Shepherd (1754-?)	uncle	Tealby
James Cropper (1781-?)	brother-in-law	Leasingham
John Cropper (1805-?)	nephew	Leasingham
Francis Gunnell	father of brother-in-law	Barrow on Humber
John Gunnell	brother of his brother-in-law	Tealby
John Hollingsworth	husband of wife's great great aunt	Leasingham

Abbreviations
LAO   Lincolnshire Archives Office
N.G.R.   National Grid Reference
O.S.   Ordnance Survey

Notes

1. Shorter, Alfred H., 1957, *Papermills and Papermakers in England 1495-1800* The Paper Publications Society, Hilversum, Holland.
2. LAO Tennyson d'Eyncourt Collection - 2 T d'E D/4
3. LAO Admon. 1718/61
4. Masters and Apprentices Revenue Records Vol. 1R 1/1 entry 169/29
5. LAO Admon.1721/61
6. LAO Tennyson d'Eyncourt Collection - T d'E G 3/15/a
7. Shorter *op. cit.*
8. *ibid*
9. Sun Fire Insurance Policy No. 86295
10. Sun Fire Insurance Policy No. 147458
11. Simmons Collection: from 1930s; Museum of Lincolnshire Life.
12. Sun Fire Insurance Policy No. 259371
13. Sun Fire Insurance Policy No. 428561
14. *The London Gazette* 29 November 1788
15. LAO Admons 1827/47
16. Sun Fire Insurance Policy No. 320103
17. Sun Fire Insurance Policy No. 358274
18. LAO - LQS Land Tax Walshcroft
19. Sun Fire Insurance Policy No. 627061
20. LAO Tennyson d'Eyncourt Collection T d'E F 9/29
21. *The London Gazette* -9 June 1826
22. Norwich Union Fire Insurance Policy No. 137131
23. LAO Tennyson d'Eyncourt Collection 2 T d'E/D/7
24. at Peckwash Mill
25. Helpston was later in Northamptonshire, but is now in Cambridgeshire. The village is situated about six miles ESE of Stamford. The Lincolnshire Twitch Paper Company was founded in the 1850s using twitch or couch grass supplied by local farmers to make brown paper and millboard. However the final product was unsuitable because it was subject to mildew. The original company was wound up in 1861. The site was bought and continued to make paper and paper products until very recently.
26. Actually, Mark's father, Thomas, was also a papermaker in Tealby.
27. manila hemp
28. 1861
29. Adam Clarke lived in style at Duffield House, Town Street in 1881
30. LAO Tennyson d'Eyncourt Collection F9/18 and F9/22
31. County Fire Office Policy 135324
32. Apprentices of Great Britain 51/89 (1750)
33. *The London Gazette* -9 June 1829
34. Sun Fire Insurance Policy No. 97091
35. Royal Exchange Fire Insurance Policy No. 181475
36. Sun Fire Insurance Policy No. 102178
37. Sun Fire Insurance Policy No. 349186
38. Sun Fire Insurance Policy No. 531539
39. Royal Exchange Fire Insurance Policy No. 136495
40. Pigot's Directory, 1830
41. Royal Exchange Fire Insurance Policy No. 149273
42. *The London Gazette* 15 May 1798
43. *The London Gazette* 17.March.1800
44. Sun Fire Insurance Policy No. 428561
45. *The London Gazette*, 29 November 1788
46. LAO Admons. 1827/47
47. Sun Fire Insurance Policy No. 102777

Bibliography

Ackrill, Enid, and others, 1980, *A Town Called Louth*, Louth Teachers Centre.

Anon, 1908, A Remarkable Paper-making Family in *The Paper-Maker and British Paper Trade Journal*, pp 460-461

Binall, P. B. G., 1943, The Weird Wigelsworths in *Goulding's Illustrated Household Almanack*, Louth.

Exley Papers, L.A.O. (Exley 16/4 Papermills) and Lincoln Central Library

Guildhall Library, Corporation of London - Insurance Policies

Harris, Colin, 1999, *Stowford Papermill*, Halsgrove

Leach, T. R., 1990, *Lincolnshire Country Houses and their Families (Part 1)*, Laece Books, Dunholme

Maddison, A. R., 1904, *Lincolnshire Pedigrees Vol. 4.*

Piercy, John, S., 1828, *The History of Retford.*

Porter, H., 1938, The Old Papermill in *The Lincolnshire Magazine* Vol. 3 No 12

Russell, Rex, C., 1988, *Aspects of the History of Barrow on Humber c1713 to 1851*, Joyce Martin

Simmons Collection: from 1930s located in the Museum of Lincolnshire Life

Shorter, Alfred, H., 1957, *Papermills and Papermakers in England 1495-1800*, The Paper Publications Society, Hilversum, Holland.

Shorter, Alfred, H., 1993, *Studies on the History of Paper Making in the British Isles*, Ashgate

Swaby, J. E., 1951, *History of Louth*, A. Brown and Sons Ltd.

Warner, K., n.d., *Why do they call the Old Mill the Paper Mill? Nobody seems to know*, Certificate in Higher Education (Local History)

Index